Peter Mason is known for his lively radio programmes with the Australian Broadcasting Corporation's Science Unit and for his books *Genesis to Jupiter*, *Cauchu – the Weeping Wood* and *The Light Fantastic*.

His research career began at the age of eleven, when he silvered copper coins for his friends, and it almost terminated in the same year with an unexpectedly effective experiment on the combustion of hydrogen.

Graduating from London University during the war, he worked on quartz crystals for radar sets to be used in the invasion of Normandy. As soon as the war ended, he changed to more peaceful avenues of research, physical problems involved in buildings and roads, in rubbers and plastics. A growing interest in biological molecules took him to the CSIRO in Australia to study the proteins in wool, and in 1966 he was invited to the foundation chair of physics in Macquarie University.

Peter Mason is vice-president of the Australian Institute of Nuclear Science and Engineering, and a member of Scientists against Nuclear Arms. His current research lies in trying to find how the cells of the brain control the temperature of the human body. He has been known to claim himself as the best footballer among the biophysicists and the best biophysicist among the footballers.

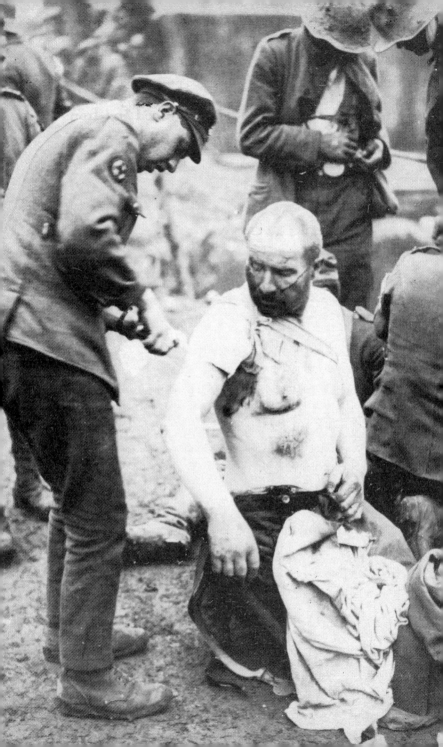

Blood
and Iron

Peter Mason

Penguin Books

Penguin Books Australia Ltd,
487 Maroondah Highway, 3134, Australia
P.O. Box 257
Ringwood, Victoria, 3134, Australia
Penguin Books Ltd,
Harmondsworth, Middlesex, England
Penguin Books,
40 West 23rd Street, New York, N.Y. 10010, U.S.A.
Penguin Books Canada Ltd,
2801 John Street, Markham, Ontario, Canada
Penguin (N.Z.) Ltd,
182-190 Wairau Road, Auckland 10, New Zealand

First published by Penguin Books Australia, 1984

Copyright © Peter Mason, 1984

Typeset in Bembo by Abb-Typesetting

Made and printed in Australia by
Dominion Press — Hedges & Bell

CIP

Mason, Peter, 1922–
   Blood and iron.

   Includes index.
   ISBN 0 14 007149 0.

   1. Krupp family. 2. Munitions - Germany.
   I. Title

338.7'6234'0922

Contents

Mixed in with the historical figures in this book are some ordinary people, the kind whose lives have been torn apart by warfare through the ages and to whom the book should be dedicated. Their names and many of the events described are, of course, fictitious; I was not present, for example, in Richard Wagner's bedroom on the morning of 5 January 1871, nor did I overhear (though I might have done) what Einstein said to Marie Curie on a terrace in Geneva in 1926. A painting can be more valid than a photograph, however, and that is the way I look at history.

PM

ONE
Krupp Go Home!

'Gold is for the mistress – silver for the maid –
Copper for the craftsman cunning at his trade.'
'Good!' said the Baron, sitting in his hall,
'But Iron – Cold Iron – is master of them all.'

Rudyard Kipling, 'Cold Iron'

The link between blood and iron is a very old idea – more than 2000 years old. The ancient Hindu remedy for anaemia, *Lauha Bhasma*, was a mixture of finely powered iron in oil, whey, vinegar, cow's urine and milk. The Greeks treated weakness with medicines containing iron, which they also called Mars; they believed that its strength came from Mars, the god of war.

Quite a bit less than 2000 years ago, it was common to dole out an iron 'tonic' if you were feeling low or weak. But in the last few years it has been realized that you can have too much of a good thing. Iron not only peps you up, but can also pep up invading bacteria and turn a moderate infection into a raging disease. It is directly involved in that curse of Western civilization, rheumatoid arthritis. In our exquisitely evolved immune system, it may be critical to the balance between a healthy organism, an infection, and cancer.

The link between blood and iron is not just thousands but millions of years old. Iron is a vital weapon in our defence system: too much of it can lead to our destruction. It is rather like the complex relations between armaments and employment, between peace and war, which emerged surprisingly from the story of iron and steel.

The house on the hill looked like the Baron's Hall in an old fairy tale. A blanket of snow covered the ancient sequoia trees guarding the entrance. It spread across the shrubs and lawns of the park, turning the grubby factories of Essen into silvery palaces, and it stretched

1

away as far as you could see over the valley of the Ruhr. The air was still, the sky a crisp wintry blue. Inside the great mansion a hundred servants padded around on their endless tasks. It was a February morning in 1958. But where was the owner of the mansion, the steel baron, Alfried Krupp?

Half a world away, a black limousine was drawing up outside a hotel in Melbourne. The air was warm and still, the sky a brilliant summery blue. A tall, immaculately dressed man emerged. He would have arrested attention anywhere. His straight, dark hair, brushed flat and parted on the right, his long thin face, with its high forehead and bushy eyebrows, his precise manner of moving, all suggested the arrival of a distinguished European gentleman. But neither these nor his more personal attributes – the look in his deep-set eyes or the tenseness of his mouth – could account for the scene that greeted him.

Outside the hotel the pavement had been cleared by a squad of policemen holding back angry demonstrators on each side. They carried placards saying, '*Achtung, Belsen!*' or 'Go home War Criminal Krupp', and they shouted, 'Butcher!', 'Jew-killer', or 'Murderer', as he walked calmly into the hotel. Pausing a moment he said, 'I am sorry that some people in Australia do not want me here.'

Why such a fuss? Surely here was a man to be admired, a model for any enterprising youth. In 1951 he had been a pauper, just released from jail; today he was one of the few men in the world who could write a personal cheque for a billion dollars.

The reason for the fuss wasn't simple. One protestor had lost a leg in the Western Desert, facing Krupp guns and Krupp tanks. Another was a woman whose husband died in a sea of burning oil when his ship was hit by a Krupp torpedo fired from a Krupp U-boat. An old Jew remembered the automatic weapons factory which Alfried set up *inside* the barbed wire of Auschwitz to ensure himself a constant supply of labourers. A Polish woman in a black shawl recalled Krupp's concentration camp for children under four – the children of the slave workers in his factories at Essen. A steelworker from Broken Hill Proprietary, Australia's biggest steelmaker, feared that Krupp was really here with the intention of taking over the Australian company. A Labour politician saw Krupp as the ex-SS man, the friend and financier of Hitler.

The roots of the rage and anguish that the sight of Krupp aroused lay in the little town of Essen, where Anton Krupp the gunsmith

The Villa Hügel. Home of four generations of Krupp patriarchs: Alfred, Fritz, Gustav and Alfried

lived three centuries ago. This Krupp made his distinctive contribution to the Thirty Years War by turning out iron gun barrels at the rate of one every two hours. That was perhaps the most agonizing of all wars before the bloodbaths of the twentieth century. In it almost half of Germany's population died. Famine and disease were widespread, and it slowly degenerated into meaningless destruction, even cannibalism.

For ten generations the Krupps marched step by step with the growing Industrial Revolution and played a leading role in the changeover from iron to steel. Krupp steel went into railways and bridges, ships and skyscrapers, building the brave new world. But their role in the destruction of much of that world by their steel guns, shells and tanks was far greater.

By the time of World War I the name of Krupp had become identified with the making and marketing of high-quality steel weapons. In August 1914, H. G. Wells lamented despairingly, 'At the very core of all this evil that has burst at last in world disaster lies Kruppism, this sordid, enormous trade in the instruments of death.'

The world faced a terrible dilemma. A popular theory held that building more armaments was the way to keep the peace. Many people thought that the theory had exploded with the first shot of the war. Yet 'progress' depended on a technology that was inextricably linked with warfare. In the depression years that followed, a flourishing arms industry seemed to be the only cure for unemployment.

It was not surprising, therefore, that, despite Alfried Krupp's hostile reception, many people in Australia were pleased to see him. They recognized in him the seeds of prosperity, thinking perhaps about the living conditions that hundreds of thousands of Krupp workers had traditionally enjoyed in peacetime.

Although steel production is still the hallmark of an industrial nation, it is no longer the prime example of the world's dilemma. Today the industries making aircraft, missiles, nuclear power stations and nuclear bombs all pose the same problem. Can you have ploughshares without swords? Can you have steel without blood?

In the medieval legends steel was always closely linked with blood. King Arthur drew his steel sword from the stone and led his knights on their violent quest for the Holy Grail, the cup that held Christ's blood. Siegfried forged his sword and gained magic powers from the blood of the dragon that he killed with it.

But before coming to the swords of the heroes or the guns of the Krupps, we should look more closely at the connections between iron and steel and between blood and iron.

TWO

Blood and Iron

Iron mines bring us the most precious and at the same time the worst of metals. By its help we cut into the ground, plant bushes, cultivate flourishing orchards, hew stone and build houses. But this metal also serves for war, murder and robbery.

Pliny, 1st century AD

Iron got here first. At least it was here long before blood. Scientists who study how the stars were made tell us that in the beginning energy came first, then hydrogen, then helium. Some time later came iron, a long time before life appeared on earth and an even longer time before blood. It also seems likely that iron will be here for a long time after blood has gone.

These scientists love to hold forth on what actually happened after the big bang that they say started it all. They describe the action in detail down to a tiny fraction of second. We get an impression of a burst of energy rushing out in all directions, changing into matter and back again into energy, a furious cosmic ballet with the whole *corps de ballet* coming on stage as the curtain goes up.

Electrons, photons, and a host of subatomic particles engage each other in dances so wild that their excitement reaches a point where they exchange their very identities. The first act ends after half an hour with the arrival of the two principals, the swiftest and lightest of atoms, hydrogen and helium.

The second act opens with a *pas de deux* between hydrogen and helium. They turn into stars and fuse together to create the middle-weight atoms, carbon and oxygen, for example, and that vital metal of war and peace, iron. In the last act the ageing stars start exploding, and the intense heat creates the heaviest elements, such as uranium and gold.

Although we may smile at these scientists, talking as if they can really understand what 'the beginning' means, their technical achievement in mapping out the evolution of matter and energy is immense. It turns out that hydrogen and helium are still far and away the most common of the elements. Taken together they form 99 per cent of the universe, leaving only 1 per cent for all of the other hundred or so elements put together, including iron.

But that's all rather remote; let's bring it nearer to home.

For each 60 kilograms of matter in the universe there are about 20 grams of iron. A 60 kilogram person may contain about 5 grams – roughly the same proportion. But for every 60 kilograms of our Earth there are nearly 30 kilograms of iron. Nearly half the Earth is iron? Yes, because the core of the Earth – out to more than half way from the centre – is a huge ball of metal, most of which is iron.

The outer layer of the Earth, a 'crust' some 30 kilometres thick, has largely the same composition as sand, with aluminium (8%) and iron (5%) making up most of the remainder. Very roughly speaking, however, you could say that we are living on an iron planet. But how did iron come to be a vital component of our blood?

Life began on Earth 3000 million years ago, perhaps in the warm seas or on clay covered rocks in the shallows. There is much speculation about how the early molecules of life were formed. Some say by 'chance', others by a 'creator'.

But one crucial step in our evolution from those primeval organisms is not so controversial. About 200 million years ago, mammals started to develop. They had a warm bloodstream and a way of keeping their temperature constant. This gave them a huge advantage over the reptiles, which were helpless in cold weather. Snakes wound round a music-hall dancer's neck should not worry you. They have been kept in the fridge until their reactions are so slow that they are no longer dangerous.

Survival clearly depended upon speed. And quick-acting brains and muscles needed far more oxygen than the body fluids could hold in solution. Somehow the warm blood had to collect this oxygen and transport it from the lungs to the places where it was urgently needed. To do this the blood cells evolved a special sort of molecular carrier-bag equipped with metal atoms to hold on to the oxygen. In human blood this carrier is called *haemoglobin*. It is a neat little structure, made from the four common atoms of life – carbon, hydrogen, oxygen and nitrogen. At its centre lie the vital oxygen-carriers, four atoms of iron. Each of these latches on to a molecule of oxygen in the lungs and releases it in the oxygen-starved regions where it is most needed. We red-blooded humans thus had iron built into our systems long before we came to realize its value to us in the arts of war and peace.

If you don't get enough oxygen, the brain is the first thing to suffer. Dizziness, failing judgement and black-out soon follow. Just before World War II, the problems of respiration, of oxygen-carrying by iron, and so forth, were being studied at the usual leisurely academic pace. But with air fighting going on in Spain and the prospect of even bloodier air battles in the war that was looming, money and machines suddenly became available for research.

In air combat it is fatal to let the enemy get above you. During the 1930s, pilots in their flying helmets and goggles simply faded out above about 3000 metres; the air got thinner, and there was not enough oxygen in each breath. An understanding of the physiology might enable you to improve the condition of the pilot's blood or to design such things as oxygen masks and pressurized flying suits. Any knowledge that would gain even 100 metres over the opposition was priceless. More precisely, its price was now paid cheerfully, although little had been forthcoming when the beneficiaries were only mountain-climbers or people suffering from respiratory ailments. Science for killing is often given a higher priority than science for living.

Haemoglobin not only carries our oxygen but also, because of its iron, gives the bright red colour to our blood.

In Goethe's epic story of Faust the devil persuades Dr Faust to sign away his soul in letters of blood. '*Blut ist ein ganz besonders Saft*', he explains – blood is a very special juice. It is, indeed, and iron is its most special ingredient.

Whether for war or for peace, iron was a difficult metal to master. Copper was more easily worked. It was the favourite metal of the civilization that slowly emerged from the stone ages, but when it came to such tough jobs as building the Pyramids, tools were needed with an edge that remained sharp. Copper was just too soft. With uncanny skill, the coppersmiths discovered how to improve the hardness of their copper tools by mixing in from 5 to 20 per cent of an even softer metal, tin. The resulting alloy, *bronze*, rapidly became the fashion in the Mediterranean lands 4000 years ago. The bronze-workers travelled great distances to get their tin, and they spread the knowledge of their trade as they went. The rich tin mines of far-off Cornwall were a great attraction, and bronze weapons from 1800 BC have been found in Britain.

The arts of bronze-working grew to include weapons, tools, armour and even statues such as the Colossus that reputedly straddled the harbour mouth at Rhodes in 300 BC. Rumour has it that a replacement statue is to be erected as a tourist attraction: in keeping with the times it will be in aluminium instead of bronze, and there is to be a cocktail bar in its head.

The Chinese were probably the finest bronze-workers of all. The finest Chinese bronzes are about 3500 years old, roughly the same age as Stonehenge. Analysis has shown that they contain almost exactly 15 per cent of tin. In that proportion bronze is nearly three times as hard as copper, and the sharpness of the bronze casting is at its best.

But the rival that would dwarf the use of bronze was already flourishing in China. The Chinese mastery of iron showed in their use of it not only for such commonplace purposes as stoves and ploughs but also for works of art.

The secrets of iron-working were also being explored in the wild mountain lands of Anatolia, today that part of Turkey bordering on Iran and Iraq. The Hittites, a warlike tribe given to riding around furiously in chariots, found that they could make a hard, grey metal by heating iron ore with charcoal in open pits. Although the fire was made hotter by blowing air on it with a bellows, it was still not hot enough to melt the iron into a flowing liquid that could be poured off. Copper was molten by 1100°C, but iron remained solid until a little over 1500°C. The Hittites extracted it from their furnaces as a pasty lump weighing a kilogram or two, and gave it a good hammering to get rid of the impurities. A final, more skilful, hammering process, *forging*, then shaped the iron into the desired object. The tough metal this method produced was later referred to as *wrought iron* because of the amount of work it needed in the hammering; 'wrought' comes from the Old English 'geworht' meaning 'worked'.

With their iron weapons and armour, the Hittites became the superpower of their time. They drove back the mighty empire of Egypt, and they so impressed the Pharaoh with their new armaments that he sent his agents to negotiate terms for the secret of the magic metal.

The new iron swords were usually not a patch on the bronze. The secret of their success lay in the wide availability of iron ore, as well as in the ease with which they could be made. Although the hammering drove most of the impurities out of the iron, enough remained to weaken the blade. But a thousand imperfect iron blades were more than a match for ten bronze, such supermen of the silver screen as Douglas Fairbanks and Errol Flynn notwithstanding. Technology was starting on its historic mission – to spread wide the powers and advantages previously enjoyed by only the few.

Bronze itself had never been available for the common people; they had always been forced to rely upon wood and stone for their weapons and tools. The advent of iron not only paved the way for cheap swords but also introduced a valuable new character to civilization – the village smith. While charioteers like the Hittites and pirates such as the Philistines were completing their conquests and settling down to fighting among themselves, a peasant culture was growing up with its ploughs, axes, and tools all made of iron.

Iron was transforming the ways of peace as well as the ways of war. In the first century AD the Roman historian Pliny the Elder described this magic metal as the most useful and the most lethal of all human discoveries.

In 1961 some strange evidence of the Roman use of iron was uncovered at the site of Agricola's headquarters near Perth in Scotland. In AD 71 his legion had been driven out by the aboriginal British. Before they left, they destroyed everything that might have been of use to their enemy. One load, too heavy to remove in their hasty departure, was buried in a pit and covered with a couple of metres of earth. The archaeologists uncovering this cache were astonished to find that it consisted of 7 tonnes of nails: they ranged from a million small nails to a thousand or so 40 centimetre long spikes. All of them had been made in the usual way – by hammering the impurities out of a spongy mass of hot iron – but the carbon content was so variable that the composition ranged from pure iron to high-carbon steel.

Despite the imperfections of the iron swords, there were always some smiths who saw the potential of iron and set out to find ways of realizing it. They were the forerunners of the military scientists of today: the metals they invented were intended primarily for war. In China, Egypt, and India they discovered how to make iron swords tougher and more deadly. The methods were secret, but the idea was to *carbonize* the iron by heating it in charcoal; to retain its new hardness by *quenching;* and finally to *temper* it in a mild heating process which sacrificed a little hardness to gain the desired toughness.

It is often asserted that the Japanese samurai swords were quenched by plunging the hot blade into the body of a prisoner. But however devious or perverted the method used, the real secret was to introduce a small amount of carbon into the iron – usually less than 1 per cent – and thereby change it into an iron-carbon alloy called a *steel*.

In many cultures the master swordsmiths learned the art of making a steel sword by heating an iron strip in carbon, folding it over, beating it with a hammer and repeating the process several times. Without knowing the actual amount of carbon that had combined, or being able to measure the temperature, the process was a chancy one. The few swords that happened to get perfectly heat-treated, like King Arthur's Excalibur, became legends.

Long before those times the Chinese had taken a giant stride ahead into iron. They mixed coal with the iron ore in their furnaces and blew air continuously through the mixture with bellows. The burning coal generated so much heat that the iron actually melted and combined with about 4 per cent of carbon. The liquid iron was poured off into moulds to make castings of the hard, brittle material, *cast iron*.

Sometimes, for special purposes requiring more toughness, it was 'puddled' about with a rod until the carbon had been burned off and the remaining pure material could be hammered into objects of wrought iron. By AD 100 the Chinese had developed their furnaces to the point where they were controlling the carbon content to between 0.5 and 1.5 per cent. Many of the steels they made then were of better quality than the steel in today's ball bearings.

It was over 1000 years before the Europeans developed a blast furnace that could actually melt the iron. The technique spread out from its origins in the Rhineland until, by the year 1600, iron was being poured out by the tonne instead of being beaten out in charges of 40 or 50 kilograms at a time.

Whole forests were cut down to feed the blast furnaces' ravenous appetite for charcoal, the charred wood that was being used in preference to coal. The little country of England was faced with the loss of the tree-clad Weald of Sussex and Surrey. In 1584 Queen

Elizabeth passed laws restricting the use of wood, not so much to preserve the beauty of her southern counties as to protect supplies for the shipbuilders of her navy. With their huge forests, both Sweden and Russia became world powers. They sold the wood that made the iron that cast the cannons that spilt the blood. And in a fashion worthy of the twentieth century, the guns were sold to whoever would pay for them. It came as no surprise when the galleons of the Armada or the troops of the Bey of Tunis opened fire on their English enemies with cannon cast in Sussex.

Even in those days gun-smithing and iron-founding were far from quiet occupations. When Dante visited the Great Arsenal of Venice two centuries earlier, his first thought was that he had arrived in hell. From its size and its din he could scarcely distinguish it from the Fifth Abyss of the Inferno, the place where politicians and senior civil servants lay in a bath of molten pitch. But in 1600 Galileo found the bustle exciting, and the skills of the Arsenal's workmen gave him the inspiration to apply his mathematics to their work of making weapons and building ships. His studies of the dynamics of projectiles and the strength of materials became the launching pad for three centuries of what we now call modern science.

That was one foretaste of the twentieth century. Another was about to descend on Europe, particularly on the iron-making states of Germany, in the form of the Thirty Years War. From 1618 to 1648 armies from France, Spain, Denmark, Sweden and Bohemia stormed over that unhappy land.

In the middle of all this, on the banks of the River Ruhr, lay the little town of Essen. The two dozen gunsmiths who lived in Essen found their situation hard but not entirely unprofitable. One of them had got off on the wrong foot, getting into various sorts of trouble and even being fined 'for beating Dr Hasselman in the street'. He redeemed himself by marrying a prominent gunsmith's daughter and went on to build up his own business until he was selling 1000 gun barrels a year. His family name would re-emerge during the Napoleonic wars and run like a sinister thread through the nineteenth and twentieth centuries of blood and iron. The eminent burgher was the gunsmith, Herr Anton Krupp.

Meanwhile, in England, two physicians were advancing our

knowledge of iron and blood. William Gilbert was studying the magnetism of iron, while William Harvey was producing a revolutionary theory about blood. In 1628 Harvey showed that the blood is pumped continuously around the body, leaving from one side of the heart and returning to the other. During exercise the rate of flow can exceed that of a kitchen tap turned full on.

Medical science was unprepared for this brilliant theory. But it pointed the way towards the technique of blood transfusion into a vein, one of the great life-saving techniques of the twentieth century. Traditionally it had been assumed that the way to benefit from someone else's blood was to drink it. After Harvey, a few brave spirits carried out experiments, as on a famous occasion at the Royal Society in 1667 when some sheep's blood was transfused into a man. The man survived, getting 20 shillings for his pains, and Samuel Pepys remarked that the business gave rise to many pretty ideas, such as letting the blood of a Quaker into an Archbishop, and so forth.

But other experiments were, regrettably, less successful, and the technique faded out. Its revival had to wait over two hundred years for Karl Landsteiner's discovery that human beings can be divided into four groups according to the composition of their blood. People in group A have a particular component that controls the tendency of their red cells to clump together into a clot; group B has a different component; a few people, in group AB, have both of these components; and about half of us, in group O, have neither. The vital discovery was that the groups are not generally interchangeable: for instance, transfusion from an A, B, or AB blood donor into an O-group recipient will develop a reaction which can be fatal.

Over two centuries were to elapse between Pepys and Landsteiner. In the meantime the European development of iron-making and iron-working, above all for the purposes of war, went steadily on until, around the middle of the eighteenth century, the first rumblings of the Industrial Revolution began to shake the world.

THREE

Iron and Steel

Huntsman's patient efforts entitle him to an elevated niche among
the heroes of industry. The invention of cast steel was second in
importance to no previous event in the world's history, unless it
may have been the invention of printing.

Nineteenth-century American industrialist

The only country ready to launch an industrial revolution was
Britain. It would need vast quantities of iron, so the foundries would
need vast quantities of wood charcoal to melt the iron ore. The
woodlands had already been stripped of their trees, so how was the
iron to be made?

Abraham Darby solved the problem in 1713 by showing how iron
could be produced in a very hot blast furnace by burning coke instead
of charcoal. Coal had been tried as a substitute for charcoal, but it
produced a very inferior iron. Coke is to coal as charcoal is to wood:
it is made by heating coal in an oven to drive off the volatile components and leave it in the form of grey, porous, metallic-looking lumps.
The undesirable sulphur and phosphorus have been burned off, and
the coke is essentially carbon.

In the blast furnace the coke burns, providing heat. It also
combines chemically with the oxygen of the iron ore to set free the
pure iron. This process of producing a metal from its ore by a combination of heating and chemical reaction is known as *smelting*. To
remove the other impurities, mainly oxides of other metals in the
original ore, lime is added to the charge in the furnace. Its role is that
of a *flux*. It fuses with these oxides, and the fused mass separates as a
molten glass-like material called *slag*.

Abraham Darby came from a family of Quakers, successful
business people who stubbornly refused to profit from the lucrative
war trade. During the American War of Independence his son,
Abraham Darby II, devoted himself to building the world's first
iron bridge, spanning the river Severn near the family works at

Coalbrookdale. It is still in use in the little town of Ironbridge.

Darby's coke-smelting process had solved the supply problem for cast iron, which was a useful material, although for many purposes it was too brittle. The growing demand for the tougher wrought iron led to a new technique. 'Cort's puddling process' was actually discovered by several ironworkers at about the same time although the ironmaster Henry Cort was the only one to get his name on it. The iron ore was heated by the gases in a 'reverberatory furnace' so that it never came into direct contact with the solid fuel. When the ore had melted into a hot puddle, it was raked around on its shallow bed by a man with a stirring rod or *rabbler* until a pasty 50 kilogram lump of nearly pure iron could be grabbed by a long pair of tongs and lifted out. The *puddler*, sweating away at perhaps the heaviest routine task ever devised, became one of the key industrial workers over the following century.

The hot lump of iron was put under the hammer to drive out slag, then forced through grooved rolls into its final shape. This turned out later to be an ideal way of making railway lines, although apart from the use of trucks in coal mines, no one had yet invented the railway.

Iron was increasingly in demand, not only for guns and bridges but also to build the Newcomen steam engines that were pumping out the water as the mines went ever deeper and deeper. A young instrument mechanic at the University of Glasgow named James Watt discovered a way of making steam engines far more efficient. He went into partnership with the prosperous Birmingham manufacturer Matthew Boulton 'to produce engines for all the world'.

By the end of the eighteenth century, while Napoleon was fighting his way across Europe, Boulton and Watt engines were to be found in paper mills and breweries, in corn mills and iron foundries. Above all, they powered the cotton mills that were the vanguard of the Industrial Revolution. But the new power was not solely at the service of peace. That prosperous city of Birmingham also made most of the British weapons for the Napoleonic wars that spanned a generation.

While James Watt was creating the prime mover for the factories and railways of the future, a Yorkshire clockmaker was discovering how to produce the most important material they would need.

Benjamin Huntsman was another successful Quaker businessman, growing up in the Lincolnshire village where he went to school with

John Wesley. After his apprenticeship to a clockmaker for a premium of four pounds, he set up his own shop and straightaway charged his apprentice twenty.

He soon became disenchanted with the quality of the steel then available. The very best was *shear steel*, which was made by heating iron bars in charcoal then repeatedly hammering, folding and reheating them. It was good metal for knife blades and swords but not uniform enough to make a reliable clock spring. Why not first melt the steel down, he asked himself, so that the carbon becomes uniformly distributed throughout the liquid?

The coke blast furnaces developed since Darby's discovery thirty years earlier were certainly capable of melting the steel. The problem was to discover a container that could withstand the fierce attack of the molten metal. Huntsman worked on the problem in a small foundry attached to his house and succeeded in making crucibles which could do the job. He used a blend of clays from different parts of England which had to be mixed and kneaded into the right consistency for moulding the crucible or 'pot'. The pot-maker carried out this skilled process of kneading by treading the wet mixture with bare feet for an hour or more until all inclusions and air-bubbles had been removed.

An air-dried pot would be loaded with about 20 kilograms of fragments made by smashing a crude steel bar on the anvil, sealed tightly to keep the air out and then brought up to a white heat in the furnace. As the steel melted, the slag rose to the top. At the right moment the crucible was lifted out, the slag was skimmed from the surface and the steel poured into a mould to form an ingot. One of the lost arts of Asia had been rediscovered.

In retrospect it may look a trivial matter to refine steel by cooking it in a clay pot and pouring off the pure liquid into a mould. Far from it. Without the modern understanding of composition or structure, and without any ability to measure the temperature more accurately than by judging the redness of the glowing crucibles, the ironmasters of Europe experimented in vain for fifty years while Sheffield built up its monopoly of crucible steel and at the same time its worldwide reputation as the City of Steel, a reputation it still has for quality, though no longer for quantity.

By the end of the eighteenth century, the European ironmasters were getting desperate. Their foundries were producing cast iron in profusion but, for the guns and machines of the dawning industrial

A steel crucible maker treading the wet clay to exactly the right consistency for moulding

age, this metal was too brittle. Wrought iron was too soft. The steel bars they could produce by the old methods were too small and could neither be welded together nor melted and cast as a large ingot without being ruined by combination with oxygen from the air. Cast steel they had to have.

French science made a brave attempt to come to the rescue. In 1789, at the outset of the French Revolution, Claude Berthollet published a book on the nature of steel showing that it was simply a compound of iron and carbon. But theory builds neither guns nor machines, and that brought them no nearer to a practical solution. When Nelson imposed a blockade after his victory at Trafalgar, Napoleon was driven to offering a prize of 4000 francs to the first steelmaker who could match the quality of Huntsman's cast steel.

By 1812 the French were retreating from Moscow. Claims for Napoleon's prize had come from several countries, although it was not awarded: presumably Napoleon had other things on his mind. The most ominous claim, could he but read the signs, had come in from Germany. Young Friedrich Krupp, five generations down from the gunsmith of Essen, had brought the family fortunes to the edge of bankruptcy and was pinning his last hopes on discovering the elusive *Geheimnis des Gusstahls*, the secret of cast steel. Brimming with confidence, he had just founded the Krupp Cast Steel Works in a small shed next to his languishing business in Essen.

Whether Friedrich Krupp actually did make cast steel at that time is uncertain. Even the quality of the steel he was selling when he died in 1826, leaving his tottering enterprise in the hands of his fourteen-year-old son, is open to doubt. What is beyond doubt, however, is the quality and achievement of that fourteen-year-old boy, Alfred, soon to be christened 'The Cannon King'.

Alfred's natural abilities were supplemented by one further advantage denied to his father – he was born at the right time. Even as he was walking behind his father's coffin, in the distance the whistle of the first Prussian railway train could be heard, hauling trucks of coal to the factories and foundries of the Ruhr. The Railway Era had begun. With Richard Trevithick's high-pressure steam engines, locomotives could now be made light enough to run on iron rails without breaking them. The heavy Boulton and Watt engines found satisfactory homes in factories and sea-going ships.

The railways had grown out of the increasing mastery of iron, and they repaid their debt handsomely. Over the next twenty years, they trebled the production of coal and iron in Britain alone, creating a huge market for that hitherto minor commodity, steel. This was capitalism in its adolescence, and there is little wonder that Marx called the railways its crowning achievement. Hard on the heels of the shrewd Quakers, investors and speculators poured their capital into the railways, eager to grasp at any chance of getting more than the 3 or 4 per cent yielded by public stock. Much of this investment sank without trace as the more hare-brained schemes of the great railway mania of 1845-47 collapsed, leaving the British railway network almost as it is today.

In the spring of 1870 it was the Grand Central Railway that brought Maurice Dupont from London to Sheffield. The Printers Association of Paris had sent him. His mission: to exchange experiences with printing workers on the problems of setting up a union to protect their interests. He began by visiting the Working Men's Association in Berlin, and they had urged him to go on to London. In London they had simply said to him, Dronfield. William Dronfield of Sheffield. He's the man you must talk to.

'Why Dronfield?' he'd asked.

Well, for a start, Dronfield was the first union secretary to win the weekly half-day holiday for his members. Since then he'd become the national secretary of the Alliance of Organized Trades. 'What's more,' they told him, 'he's the agent for A. J. Mundella, a radical mill-owner and a Member of Parliament. The pair of them have been campaigning on public health and wider voting rights, and now they're trying to get the school leaving age pushed up from eight to ten. Bill Dronfield knows about unions, and he knows about politics. He's the man you must talk to.'

He'd come to Sheffield, tired and grimy, with specks of carbon in his hair, nose and clothes. A quick wash, and he was in a pub sitting opposite the chubby Yorkshireman.

'It's not the beer talking,' he said, reading Maurice's thoughts. 'We're used to beer in Sheffield. The lads in the foundries drink it all day. It's the only way they can keep going in that heat, and it's a sort of habit for us now in the evenings. I tell you education's what'll save this country. How can you expect the workers to co-operate intelligently as long as they're kept ignorant?'

Maurice asked him about the violence against non-unionists and their employers. 'Was it true that machines had been broken, tools and equipment stolen?' he enquired.

'It's true enough,' growled Dronfield. 'They even got to shooting and blowing up houses. Just look at the millions the steel firms made out of the Crimea and the Civil War in America. Where would John Browns, or Firths, or Vickers be without the guns and the battle-ships? And where would the workers be when half the jobs were gone?' Draining his glass, he concluded, 'Education's the only way to get people able to understand. And that's the next thing your union can work for when you've won yourselves some decent conditions of work and pay.'

Maurice Dupont shut his eyes and finished his beer before replenishing the glasses. 'Before I leave England', he said at length, 'I would like to visit one of your famous cutlery works; or, perhaps, one of the places where they make the Sheffield steel. Do you think that could be possible?'

Dronfield seemed amused at the suggestion. 'I don't think it would be very kind to send you off with a lungful of grit! The grinding shops are about the most unhealthy places in the country. But I think we could fix you up with a sight of cast steel being made; and that's the best in the whole world. I tell you what, young sir, I'll do you a special favour for the sake of our international brotherhood. I'll call for you at six in the morning, and we'll go up on the train to Abbey foundry at Attercliffe. If we're lucky we might even see a teeming. They'll be pouring the liquid steel from the crucible into the mould', he added, noticing Maurice's puzzled face.

Maurice would not forget the next morning, even through the months of war, bombardment and fighting that lay ahead. He had waited outside the foundry while Dronfield went in and came out again a few minutes later with John Lovedale. John was the teemer, the man who poured the molten metal and who was in charge of a small group. 'Eh', said Lovedale, 'you've timed it well. We've a big shipbuilder's order in so we kept the furnace going overnight. First two pots should be ready for teeming very soon. Come on in. I'll not show you the pots being made, but you're welcome to have a look at everything else. Perhaps you can give us a tip on the French way of doing things. And what do you know about Krupp's ways? Bill tells me you've just come from Germany.'

As they went in Maurice was murmuring that the best he could offer would be some advice on typesetting when he was hit by a wave of heat. 'Let's have your coat', said Dronfield, handing him a pair of overalls. 'You didn't really dress for this job did you?'

Dronfield led him across the room by the arm. 'You'd best keep away from those cover plates on the floor; the furnaces are under there, and that's where the pots will be lifted out when the melt is done.' Moving towards the doorway, they met a boy of about twelve coming in with a large jug of beer. 'Jim, the cellar lad', explained Dronfield, 'John Lovedale's boy; he'll likely be a teemer himself one day, if not the owner of the whole bloody foundry the way he's going.'

Taking a grateful draught of ale, Maurice no longer thought wistfully of sipping dry red wine. Jim, he could dimly see, had finished giving out the beer and was over at the far wall, sliding shut the chimney doors. Dronfield waved to him to watch carefully; the casting was about to begin. A bent and wizened little man, just forty years old, was wrapping a wet cloth round his neck, helped by Jim who was tying wet sacking round his body and legs. This was the 'puller-out', whose job was to get the pot of molten steel as far as the mould.

Lovedale had decided that the moment had come. He shouted to Jim, who reached out with a long iron rod and managed to slide the cover off one of the furnace holes in the floor. The puller-out approached the blinding glare that came from the hole and tested the pot all round with his long pair of tongs. Convinced that it was sound, he lifted the glowing pot out of its hole and lowered it carefully on his trolley. He was visibly steaming. The heat boiled the water from the sacking and stung the few areas of exposed skin. Tightly screwing up his face, he wheeled the pot across the floor and placed it with his tongs by the side of the waiting mould.

Now it was Lovedale's turn. Removing the lid, he squinted at the white-hot slag on the surface of the liquid metal. Satisfied with what he saw, although Maurice could not imagine how he wasn't completely blinded by the glare, he gripped the pot round its middle with his long pair of tongs. Leaning well back, his knees bending to balance his load of nearly 50 kilograms, he slowly twisted the pot over and began to pour. As the brilliant stream of liquid steel emerged, the puller-out skimmed the slag from the surface with a long-handled tool.

It seemed an age before the mould had been filled, but almost at once it was prised apart, the red-hot ingot was inspected by Lovedale and a mark of its quality hammered into it. The whole process now started again.

'Teeming': lifting the 30 kg crucible from the furnace and pouring the liquid steel into the mould. War-time production at Firth Brown's in Sheffield, 1940

Maurice Dupont did not stay for the rest of the ten-hour shift. Taking his farewells of Dronfield and the Lovedales, he boarded the southbound train. He would have much to report. The conditions in Sheffield had brought home to him the arguments he had heard from the little group at the Working Men's Association in Berlin. But as he leant on the rail of the pitching steamer his thoughts were far away from steel or even from printing.

He was distracted by the occasional glimpse of Calais heaving up over the prow, or Dover astern, but thoughts from his travels kept returning. The memory of a soft voice, with a captivating German intonation; a soft face in a cloud of golden hair. Walking up the Unter den Linden after one of those long meetings with the Berlin printers, they had stopped by the Brandenburger Gate. 'Lise', he'd said, 'whatever happens, after London and Paris I shall come back again.' Somehow, he thought, he must keep that promise. But how? That was to be a war and half a lifetime away.

FOUR

The Steel Fist

My appointed station in life was that of a basketmaker, and straightaway I was set to work at the elementary stages, as an informal apprentice at eightpence a week with dinner and tea – a welcome addition to the family budget. Hours were long: a day of twelve hours for us boys.

Thomas Okey, b. 1852

The social costs of the Industrial Revolution were becoming visible. The census of 1851 showed that if you were born in the Worcestershire town of Dudley your expectation of life was just eighteen and a half years. There was nothing abnormal about that; it simply reflected the high rate of infant mortality at that time. Out of every three children born in Sheffield one would die before the age of five.

And if you survived the hazards of early childhood, what was in store for you if you had no silver spoon in your mouth? One little boy could have told you, although his story had a surprise ending. Thomas Okey was the son of a basketmaker and naturally young Tom had to follow suit.

After Tom had become a basketmaker, he decided to teach himself languages. He was so adept at them that he later became the first Professor of Italian Studies at the University of Cambridge.

If you were a girl, however, no matter how good you were at languages, even the chance of getting to a university was denied to you.

The winds of social discontent were blowing strongly across Britain in those days, and as they swept through Europe they fanned a smouldering resentment. In 1848 the young Marx and Engels published the Communist Manifesto and almost simultaneously the French monarchy was overthrown. Revolt spread across Europe, engulfing a dozen states within weeks. This 'springtime of the peoples' did not last long. Within a year the old forces were back in control, Louis Napoleon in France and Bismarck in Prussia. Twenty years later the struggle between these two men formed the backdrop to the dramatic arrival of steel as a major force in warfare. Bismarck wrote the script of the drama, but the stage manager was Herr Alfred Krupp.

In 1838 Krupp had visited England in disguise. His intention: to prise out the secrets of the British steel manufacturers. But although he took out his passport in what he thought was the English-sounding name of A. Crup, his career as a spy was short-lived. It might have been because he had spent only a few weeks trying to learn the language, but also perhaps because he would insist on going around wearing a pair of spurs.

When he got back to Essen, he found that his firm was still turning a handsome profit from its normal production of items such as the hard steel rollers used for making patterned cutlery. With hard work and perfectionism in the foundry, he had at last realized his ambition of making high-quality cast steel. Despite his success, he was still trying in vain to arouse the enthusiasm of the Prussian army for his epoch-making military project: a 3 pound cast-steel cannon.

It is hardly surprising that the Prussian artillery officers resisted Krupp's proposition. Cast-iron cannon were brittle. They had a reputation for bursting in action, with dreadful consequences for the gunners. On the other hand, when a wrought-iron gun had been demonstrated aboard the world's first iron-built frigate, the USS *Princeton*, it had also blown up, killing the Secretary for the Navy. The carbon content of cast steel put it somewhere between cast iron and wrought iron. Why should they expect it to be any safer? The sensible, conservative attitude was to stay with bronze. Admittedly bronze was both expensive and heavy, but Wellington had proved its quality when he defeated Napoleon at Waterloo. The military mind has traditionally been happier to dwell on the lessons of the past war than to undergo the painful process of trying to envisage what new departures may occur in the next.

Krupp was disconsolate. Then came a startling piece of news that rekindled his hopes. In two years' time the first World's Fair was to be held at Hyde Park in London. The Great Exhibition would be housed in a huge structure of prefabricated iron girders holding 300 000 glass panes. An editorial in *Punch* sounded the right note of wonder by calling it 'The Crystal Palace'. The Astronomer Royal struck a blow at the credibility of scientists by predicting that it would fall down when the ceremonial cannon were fired. But it didn't.

Alfred Krupp now set himself to win a vitally important though unspoken contest: which European steelmaster could display the biggest ingot of cast steel? With precise Prussian discipline, he drilled his foundryworkers until they could pour ninety-eight crucibles simultaneously to cast a perfect 2000 kilogram ingot in a single piece. 'We will make the English open their eyes,' he announced to his steaming workers.

English eyes were indeed opened on that sunny May Day in 1851, when Queen Victoria arrived at Hyde Park. Dressed in pink and silver, the Queen was received by the Archbishop of Canterbury, a thousand throats gave voice to the Hallelujah Chorus, and Prince Albert, swelling with justifiable pride at the splendour of his brainchild, spoke on its great theme: progress. The exhibition of 1851, he declared, would give us a living picture of the point of development at which the whole of mankind had arrived.

He made no reference to the absence of the Chinese from their stand. They had stayed away in a silent and bitter protest against the British action in pouring massive amounts of opium into their country during the wars of the 1840s.

Of the tens of thousands of exhibits, which was the most popular? Some plumped for 'The Greek Slave', a statue by the American sculptor Hiram Powers. As a crank was turned, this unclad young woman slowly revolved on her pedestal so that she could be viewed from every angle. It was a triumph of technological voyeurism over Victorian prudery.

If you were a steelmaker, however, you really would have found something to marvel at. In the British display, Turton's of Sheffield were proudly presenting their 'Monster Casting', an ingot of 1000 kilograms of cast steel. Further on, in the Prussian section, under the sign of Friedrich Krupp of Essen, you would meet its big brother, twice its size and decorated with the medal and ribbons that Alfred Krupp had confidently anticipated.

Not everyone found the attractions of a rotating Greek slave or even a 2 tonne slab of steel irresistible, however, and for those who did not there was a bewildering array of other delights. The British wing of the Crystal Palace took pride of place, not just because Britain was the home team but because, in 1851, it was unmistakably the top dog, the leader of the booming Industrial Revolution.

There stood the Hall of Machinery, paying its homage to the origins of the revolution with a pyramid of iron ore at one side of its

The Greek slave

entrance and a single 21 tonne block of coal at the other. Inside the hall, great locomotives capable of travelling at 100 kilometres an hour steamed and hissed on their turntables; marine engines, hydraulic steam hammers and power looms shook both the floor and eardrums with their pounding.

Visions of the technological Utopia ahead sparkled amid a sea of traditional craft works on the stands of the other developing countries. France showed Daguerre's camera among its porcelain, tapestries and perfumes; Belgium a miner's safety lamp among the lace. The German states displayed Siemens's insulated wire, which was soon to be used in the transatlantic cable, by the side of their Dresden china.

The practical Americans showed Colt revolvers and rifles made by the novel techniques of mass production, and the reaping machines which were about to create a new agricultural revolution. They also displayed false teeth, cheque books, 'sensible women's garments', such as bloomers, the Morse telegraph, Singer's sewing machine and Goodyear's famous rubber room in which everything – curtains, carpets and furniture included – was made of rubber.

Exotic items had arrived from all over the world. The Bey of Tunis sent rosewater and 'two scissors used in the red cap manufacture'. There were fine swords from Toledo, black lace from Barcelona, Dutch diamonds, Havana cigars, pearls from the Indian Ocean, musk from Turkey. Canada sent a gleaming new fire engine and from Australia came hats that convicts had made from the leaves of cabbage trees. But more than any of these, the crowds besieged an item intended solely for death, and it had got there really by accident.

Transporting a 2 tonne steel ingot from Essen to London had not been an easy task. For a short while it had seemed that it could never get to the exhibition in time. A panic-stricken Alfred Krupp had cabled to Essen, 'Send whatever else can be got ready'. What could be got ready duly arrived and became Item 649 in the exhibition catalogue: 'Gun and carriage, cast-steel cuirass breastplates'. The gun was his latest pet project, his 6 pounder of cast steel. It had been polished until it shone like a mirror, and it was mounted on a platform of hand-rubbed ash. By its side, on a sea of Prussian blue velvet, gleamed the six armour breastplates of the cuirassiers. Overhead, as a canopy for the whole stand, was suspended a tent from a Prussian campaign bearing the royal flag and shield. When the steel ingot arrived, just in time to take its place of honour, the Krupp display showed the world what lay ahead.

But the world that passed through that euphoric exhibition in 1851 did not want to see what the Krupp display implied. Queen Victoria paused to admire the products of Krupp steel, and the millions who followed her caught their breath at the romantic visions of gallantry conjured up by the shiny gun, the flags and the armour. Krupp steel posed no threat to a civilized nation. Wasn't this the Age of Progress?

The shiny gun in the Prussian blue stand was the steel fist in the velvet glove, but no one saw the connection.

FIVE

Steel Forges Ahead

> The cheapening and improvement of iron and steel during the eighteenth and nineteenth centuries was the most important event of its kind in history - or perhaps just the most important event in history.
>
> James E. Gordon

Alfred Krupp sailed home across the North Sea in a subdued frame of mind. He wondered if the effort had been worthwhile. Certainly the publicity value had been immense. *Krupp* was now a name to command respect among the steelmakers of Europe. In London, thanks to the gracious attentions of Queen Victoria, it was a household word. And in the secluded private rooms of the Crystal Palace the flourishing manufacturers of railway rolling stock had showered him with orders for the Krupp bread and butter lines: cast-steel axles and springs. But something was troubling him.

His gleaming 6 pound cannon, the object of so much enthusiasm, was at this moment being packed up for shipment home. No one wanted to buy it. Surely such enthusiasm should not be wasted? He really must find a way of transmuting it into gold.

The summer of 1851 saw the forty-year-old bachelor pacing the banks of the Ruhr, watching the pall of smoke rising from his foundries now dominating the once-picturesque town of Essen. A lonely figure, marching stiffly along in his jackboots, he was wrestling with two problems: how to regain the personal services lost to him by the death of his mother, and how to sell his steel guns. The first of these was easier to solve than the second: that one involved his deepest emotions. 'Two things . . . alone can move me,' he wrote to a friend, 'honour and prosperity.'

It took him two years to find a suitable wife. In 1853 he married Bertha Eichoff who soon produced the mandatory son and heir for the Krupp dynasty, little Friedrich Alfred. The delighted father preferred the shortened form of Fritz, and that was what he used both for his son and for his newest and noisiest machine. 'The Steam-hammer Fritz will hammer away right round the clock,' he announced. 'We shall startle the Antipodes out of their slumbers.'

In the meantime he had been preparing the ground for a brilliant method for selling his guns. In 1852 he had his shining new cannon polished until it shone like a mirror, and then he presented it as a gift to the King of Prussia. The timing was perfect. The cannon would be set up in the marble hall of Potsdam castle just before the state visit of the Emperor of Russia, Czar Nicholas I. Alfred would get two sovereigns for the price of one. The Russian, moreover, was head of one of the great powers of Europe, and the potential export market was boundless.

The display in Potsdam's marble halls brought an unexpected bonus. Among the visitors who admired the gun was the Prussian King's young brother, Wilhelm Friedrich von Hohenzollern. Wilhelm had only recently returned from exile. He had been sent away for his own safety following his bloody part in suppressing the Berlin riots of 1848. As a young man he had won the Iron Cross, leading bayonet charges against the French. He was unhampered by professional military conservatism, and the prospects of steel cannon excited him. He visited the factories at Essen, decorated Alfred with a high military order and left with a clear understanding that should he become Kaiser, some lucrative orders would be coming Krupp's way.

The European industrial barometer was now starting to falter. The Iron Horse was still leading the revolution, but the basic material wasn't up to the task of providing rails, axles, wheels and springs that were reliable and safe. Under the heavy traffic, the iron rails were cracking up within a year or so of being laid. A steel horse and a steel road were needed, and the call was for more steel, better steel and, above all, cheaper steel. Yet it took a war to generate the incentive that would solve the problem of making steel cheaper.

The war that it needed, the Crimean War, started in the spring of 1854. It was launched by Britain, with the assistance of France and Sardinia, against Russia, for reasons which are unusually obscure. Russia was doing well in its latest war with Turkey and perhaps seemed likely to get too close to Constantinople for British peace of mind. At any rate, a degree of lunacy affected the participants from the start. The French court held a seance to conjure up the spirit of the dead Napoleon, while the more laconic British had a look at the map on the wall, realized that the Crimea was a peninsula and decided it would be a simple matter for the fleet to cut it off at the isthmus; only later did it dawn on them that the depth of the water on each side of the isthmus was less than a metre.

Public opinion had already been inflamed by the British newspapers, with *The Times* in the vanguard. Thomas Carlyle wrote in his diary, 'It is the idle population of editors, etc., that have done this to England.' Yet it was *The Times* war correspondent, W. H. Russell, who most strongly resisted the efforts of the British military to muzzle the despatches from the front. His vivid reports of the folly and heroism on both sides were ultimately responsible for the fall of Lord Aberdeen's government.

Russell made the charge of the Light Brigade unforgettable and, for generations, British schoolchildren were forced to chant Tennyson's poetic version:

> Half a league, half a league,
> Half a league onward.
> All in the valley of Death
> Rode the six hundred.

Theirs not to reason why, theirs but to do or die, passed into the national class-consciousness, and British military glory was enshrined in Tennyson's stanzas.

'*C'est magnifique mais ce n'est pas la guerre,*' commented General Bosquet – it was magnificent, but it wasn't war.

But was it even magnificent? When could their glory fade? asked Tennyson. The question was soon answered when the twenty survivors failed to get jobs back in England and were driven to appeal for charity. A total of twenty-four pounds was collected for them. Rudyard Kipling wrote a sardonic send-up of 'The Charge', concluding:

> They felt that life was fleeting;
>   they knew not that art was long,
> That though they were dying of famine,
>   they lived in deathless song.
> They asked for a little money to keep the wolf from the door;
> And the thirty million English sent twenty pounds and four!

In 1856 the Crimean War petered out. What was there to show for it beyond a casualty list of over half a million, mostly killed by disease? The British and Russians soon resumed their endless skirmishing over the approaches to India, taking it in turns to gain control over the fiercely independent country of Afghanistan.

The beneficiaries of the Crimean slaughter were the military, not just the generals and admirals but also the growing ranks of military suppliers and technologists. Here, perhaps, was the genesis of the military-industrial complexes of today.

One thing the war had shown was that the day of the wooden warship was over: the future lay with the ironclad. The French had brought up three floating batteries, each driven by steam and carrying eighteen 50 pounder guns. They were built from wood, but their sides were covered in iron plates 10 centimetres thick. They proved to be impervious to the Russian shells.

The British gunboats carried a different pointer to the future, the rifled cannon of Messrs Armstrong. Rifling, the cutting of a spiral groove inside the bore of a cannon, as had long been done for 'sporting' guns, doubled its range. The final step in changing from loading through the muzzle to loading through a hinged plate at the rear would be taken later by Armstrong in Newcastle and perfected by Krupp in Essen.

From the outset of the war the British had been troubled by problems with their cannon, quite apart from the usual questions of range and accuracy. Their cast-iron barrels had to be very thick to avoid bursting, and consequently the guns were very heavy. Fortunately for them, though with monumental consequences for the world at large, their problems came to the attention of a self-educated Englishman who had already found fame and fortune as an inventor. He had made a fine start to his inventive career by designing a machine to make the 'gold powder' that was then in great demand. It was used in their gold lacquer by the japanners, the craftsmen who imitated the Japanese ware now coming into the country after the forcible opening of Japan to the West. The name of the young man was Henry Bessemer.

Although the village of Charlton on the outskirts of London was bathed in sunlight, the lace curtains in the little cottage by the heath were drawn. Miss Ellen Bessemer wanted no glare on her easel or on the glass vase holding the deep red chrysanthemums which were the subject of her painting.

Unnoticed, a young man had dismounted from his horse and tethered it to the gatepost. His loud knocking brought Miss Bessemer to the door with a cry of pleasure. 'Why Henry, what's brought you out here?'

'I was just on my way down to Woolwich. There's some more trouble at the Arsenal with the iron guns. Old Mr Millington asked me to visit the foundry. Perhaps he thinks I can show him what's going wrong.'

'Really, Henry, don't be so silly. What would you know about guns? It's just that he likes talking to you. He always did. But only last week I heard that one of the guns blew up and two young lads down there were killed. So don't go taking any risks.'

'Of course I won't. But tell me, Ellen, are those your latest paintings?'

That was the opportunity Bessemer's sister had been waiting for. Happily she presented her paintings to him with a request that she had been saving up for weeks: 'Here they are, in the lovely new portfolio I've made to keep them in. And there's something you can do for me. I want you to write on it, with those elegant letters of yours, so that it says: Studies of Flowers from Nature, by Miss Bessemer.'

'That little incident was fraught with the most momentous consequences for me', Bessemer wrote later. 'In fact, it changed the whole current of my life and rendered possible that still greater change which the iron and steel industry of the world has undergone.'

During Henry's ride home, the thought of doing Ellen's lettering in gold lacquer came into his mind, and when he reached St John Street in Clerkenwell he called in at the shop of Mr Clark, a colourman, for some gold powder. Having selected two samples, he was surprised to find that he had to pay seven shillings an ounce for them. The powders were made from about six pennyworth of brass so that the value added was six shillings and sixpence – a gain of 1300 per cent! Here was his big chance. He designed a machine that eliminated the tedious and expensive hand preparation of the powdered brass. It set him on the path of invention that would culminate in the first mass production of cheap steel.

One successful invention followed another until, visiting Paris in

1854, he was received by the Emperor, Louis Napoleon III. The guns were thundering in the Crimea, and Napoleon's interest had been aroused by a report that Bessemer had designed a shell that spun on its axis, thereby gaining both stability and accuracy.

'It so happens', said Bessemer, 'that I have in my pocket a mahogany model of my rotating projectile. With your permission, I should like to present it to you.'

'Monsieur Bessemer, I am deeply obliged to you,' the Emperor replied. 'It is an elegant device. My ministers have informed me of your capabilities and I would be glad if you would continue your experiments and keep me informed of your results. I have arranged for an unlimited amount of credit to be placed at your disposal by the finance house of Baring Brothers.'

Barings of London had provided the funds the United States government needed to buy Louisiana from France in 1803; and it was they who had raised the money that the British paid for help from Russia, Austria and Prussia at the battle of Waterloo. Bessemer gratefully dipped his hand into this apparently bottomless pit of wealth and soon succeeded in producing some 30 pound rotating shells for trial. They were at once rejected by the conservative French artillery generals on the grounds that they would burst the cast-iron cannon which he had designed to fire them.

Undeterred, Bessemer turned to the problem of improving the metal of which the guns were made. He was well aware that his knowledge of iron metallurgy was not great, consisting merely of scraps of information acquired from various smiths and foundries and from his visits to Woolwich Arsenal. Yet even this apparent handicap seemed to him a source of strength: 'I had nothing to unlearn. My mind was open and free to receive any new impressions, without having to struggle against the bias which a lifelong practice of routine operations cannot fail more or less to create.'

One surprising impression he got, watching iron being smelted in a blast furnace, was that air blowing on the surface of the molten iron did not cool it but made it hotter. The extra heat came from the combustion of carbon in the iron. It dawned on him that a continuous stream of air blowing through the molten metal could not only burn up as much of the carbon as required, but also provide enough heat from the burning to complete the steelmaking process without needing any other fuel.

Back in his London home, he proceeded to design an egg-shaped furnace lined with silica bricks and open at the top. It could be filled with molten pig-iron through a trough in its side, and at the bottom there were pipes through which air could be blown. He patented the device on 9 February 1856. So was born the famous Bessemer converter, the flaming monster of the Industrial Revolution that gobbled up molten iron and spewed it out as *mild steel*.

So also was the course of history changed. The price of steel fell by 80 per cent to about £10 a tonne. Steel railways and steel guns proliferated. But first there were some difficulties to be overcome.

Henry Bessemer announced his process in a lecture to the annual meeting of the British Association for the Advancement of Science, although the editors of that august institution did not consider his contribution important enough to print. But the steelmasters received his idea with enthusiasm, and there was a rush to try out the new converters: alas, they all failed to produce good quality steel. It seemed for a time that the process would sink without trace.

In Bessemer's original experiments he had very luckily used a Swedish iron ore that was low in phosphorus. Most British ores were high in phosphorus, and the Bessemer conversion process was so rapid that little of that phosphorus was burned out. Because of this the steel turned out to be *cold short;* as in 'shortbread', the term *short* implies brittleness, and, indeed, the Bessemer steel made from high-phosphorus ore was so brittle as to be almost useless.

None of the Sheffield steel manufacturers would now go any further without a monopoly of the process, but that was more than Bessemer would concede. Confident that he was on the right track, he persuaded a group of wealthy industrialists to go into partnership with him. Together they set up a steelworks in the heart of Sheffield, talking care always to use ores that were low in phosphorus. His purpose, he said, was not to work his process as a monopoly, but simply to force the trade to adopt it by underselling them in their own market. This, he thought, the extremely low cost of production would enable him to do, while still retaining a high rate of profit on all that was produced.

A high profit was certainly what he and his partners enjoyed. Each £100 invested in 1856 produced both a capital gain of £2300 and a handsome income averaging £400 a year until they sold the business in 1870. In that year Bessemer was elected President of the Iron and Steel Institute of Great Britain. Later he became a Fellow of the Royal Society and was knighted. He was already a millionaire in nineteenth-century pounds. Looking back in later life, he calculated

Bessemer converter in full blow

that his royalties had amounted to '1,057,748 of the little gold medals issued by Her Majesty's Mint'. Steel had rewarded its greatest benefactor.

In the middle of the nineteenth century, however, the Industrial Revolution was still being built on iron. So it would largely remain for another twenty years. Although the Bessemers multiplied and rained their golden firework displays into the smoky skies over the steel cities of the world, even by 1870 only 12 per cent of the iron produced in Britain and Germany finished up as steel.

In 1856, for instance, the English engineer Isambard Kingdom Brunel, already famous as a designer of railways, bridges and guns, had turned his attention to metal ships. He had used iron for the *Great Britain*, the largest steamship afloat, and was now supervising the construction of an even larger iron ship in a yard at Millwall on the Thames. Displacing 20 000 tonnes, she would carry 4000 passengers, twice as many as the Cunard liner, *Queen Elizabeth*, a century later. Her name was to have been *Leviathan* but, in view of her intended role to link Britain with Australia and the East Indies, Brunel had it changed to the *Great Eastern*. Although she never sailed on these exotic far eastern routes, her steadiness and manoeuvrability won her one of the most important jobs of the time: laying the Atlantic cable in 1865.

Cables were starting to take the investment limelight away from the railways, but iron was still the philosopher's stone of the new breed of engineering entrepreneurs: it enabled them to make things and turn them into money. 'Wealth and rapidity are what the world now admires', wrote Germany's favourite poet, Wolfgang von Goethe, 'and what everyone strives to attain.'

Nowhere was this more apparent that in the New World. Even while Brunel was planning the astonishing feat of launching his great ship sideways into the Thames, the ebullient Walt Whitman was celebrating the brash materialism of his native land, now building its own industrial revolution out of iron: 'Colossal foundry, flaming fires . . . waste and extravagance of material, mighty castings; such is a symbol of America.'

Before long, however, the horror of the American Civil War cast a shadow over his boundless, gutsy optimism.

I was in the midst of it all – saw war where war is worst – not on the battle-fields, no – in the hospitals: there war is worst: there I mixed with it; and now I say, God damn the wars – all wars.

SIX

The Eagle Swoops

The war of 1866 did not break out because Prussia was threatened or because public opinion demanded war. It was a war for which the cabinet made long and careful preparation ... to establish Prussia as the pre-eminent power in Europe.

Field Marshal Helmuth von Moltke

In the Ruhr valley, Alfred Krupp was also feeling disgusted with war. His reason was different from Whitman's: he had failed to sell any of his cannon. True, the Egyptians had placed a small order and Napoleon III had been on the point of buying 300 of his 12 pounders. But at the crucial moment, the Emperor had yielded to political pressures. He took the order away from Krupp and placed it instead with the Le Creusot works of the Schneider family, the leading arms factory in France. The disappointed Krupp hawked his guns round Austria, Russia, and several of the Germanic states, but each time came away empty-handed.

Giving up the struggle, he decided to devote all of his efforts to the arts of peace. Apart from his springs and axles, he was riding to fortune on an invention of his very own, a cast-steel tyre for the railway wheels of the world. There he knew he was on to a winner. He was already selling over 10 000 steel tyres a year, and soon the Krupp reputation would be nailed to the mast of this single product by the adoption of the famous trademark: three intersecting circles.

But, in 1859, the weathercock of his fortunes suddenly swung round again in the winds of war. His friend Wilhelm, the Prince Regent, arranged for the Prussian War Office to order 300 of his steel 6 pounders. Six months later the Prince became King Wilhelm I of Prussia.

It is hard to comprehend the nature of the Prussian state at that time. American author William Manchester described it as 'a comic opera country led by braggarts and introspective, professorial bureaucrats'. King Wilhelm dreamed of uniting the German states into a great nation with himself at the head. He would be like Odin, the chief god in the old legends. First he would need a Thor, a thunder-god with a mighty hammer, and who better for that job than his loyal subject and friend, Alfred Krupp? For his scheming, political fire-god Loki he had the ideal choice, the Brandenburg aristocrat Otto Eduard Bismarck-Schönhausen.

'The German states look not to Prussia's liberalism, but to her force!' proclaimed Bismarck. Thanks to Krupp, they would not look in vain. With Krupp rails, Krupp trains and Krupp guns, these three godlike Prussians were about to put a new and powerful nation on the map of Europe: Germany. And Alfred, the Essen steelmaker soon to be christened by the press 'The Cannon King', would not be out of place in this exalted company.

The ten ferocious years that followed were crucial for the future of Europe, indeed, for the world. Bismarck was seeking to weld the German states into a powerful nation and Krupp was providing him with the tools for the job. Krupp's support was essential, though often erratic. He had snapped up the Prussian licence to the Bessemer process, for example, without investigating its drawbacks. He was, of course, elated by the speed of the process and the cheapness of the steel it produced, but his commercial prudence may have been paralysed by a Teutonic feeling for romantic beauty.

How he would revel in watching a Bessemer converter in action! The huge furnace tilts slowly over on its side. A stream of white hot metal – molten pig iron – is poured into its gaping mouth, and slowly it turns again until once more it points to the sky. Air is blown up into the liquid metal through pipes in the base of the furnace and the spectacular process of converting iron into steel begins.

A great shower of sparks emerges, followed by a cloud of brown fumes. For several minutes a dull red flame flickers at the mouth of the converter, telling the operators that the oxygen in the air is burning up the silicon and manganese impurities into a slag. That is the clever part of Bessemer's process: these burning reactions generate so much heat that the temperature is driven up from about 1300°C to 1600°C without any fuel being required other than the air being blown in. At the same time the unwanted carbon is also burnt into carbon dioxide, and the last glorious stages are heralded by a brilliant white flame shooting up 10 metres into the air.

Just before the white-hot metal is poured out, the sweating iron-workers throw in an amount of coal, calculated to give just the

Otto von Bismarck, Germany's Iron Chancellor

right carbon content, together with a manganese compound called spiegeleisen (mirror-iron). This unlikely sounding substance greatly improves the quality of the steel by preventing its combination with oxygen.

After the additions of coal and spiegeleisen have been made Krupp looks on in wonder as the liquid steel is cast. The whole process has taken a spellbinding half hour rather than the hours or even days taken using previous methods.

Krupp was aware that the addition of spiegeleisen had been the brilliant invention of Robert Mushet, Bessemer's one-time friend who had come to his rescue when the future of the converter seemed bleak. Their friendship ended when Bessemer started using the technique without any acknowledgement or recompense to Mushet. He could get away with this because the original patent had been badly drawn up. Only after an appeal had been made by the daughter of the impoverished Mushet did Bessemer at length concede him a pension of £300 a year.

Robert Mushet had gone on to set the engineering world on the track of the valuable class of materials known as alloy steels. Mid nineteenth-century engineers faced a serious problem with machine tools made from ordinary carbon steel which softened under the heat developed when cutting metal at high speeds. In 1868 Mushet invented an alloy of steel and tungsten which was immune to this softening and thus made a huge contribution to productivity.

Despite the impressive performance of the Bessemer converter, Alfred Krupp had become one of Bessemer's dissatisfied customers when he first brought the process to Essen in 1862. The iron ores used in the Ruhr were high in phosphorus, the very condition that was disastrous for the quality of Bessemer steel. Unfortunately, the part-time chemist who would bring his science to solve that problem with resounding success was then only fourteen years old, and the solution would not come until 1879.

In the meantime, Alfred was driven to buying up low-phosphorus iron mines in Spain. He would need to make full use of his Bessemer converters now that Bismarck's policy of military aggression was swinging into action. In 1864 Prussia launched a blitzkrieg against Denmark. This won Bismarck two more pieces for his great jigsaw of Germany: the duchies of Schleswig and Holstein. Rising patriotically to the challenge, Krupp announced to his steelworkers that they must 'put all their energies into serving Prussia quickly, and obtain as rapidly as possible what is lacking, rifling machines, and the like'.

Patriotism and profitability now lay in beautiful conjunction. The rifling machines were for the new breechloaders, and 'the like' would assuredly include machinery for producing more steel tyres for the railways. For Krupp was well aware that Helmuth von Moltke, the Prussian Chief of Staff, was a dedicated railway buff. As a youth he had invested all his savings in the Berlin-Hamburg railway, and his interest had led to his election to the Board of Directors. The skilful use that the North was making of railways in the raging American Civil War was an object lesson that he of all European soldiers could not miss. By 1866, when Bismarck was ready for his next move, the Prussian army had acquired two great strengths: the mobility of a well-planned railway system and a supply of breech-loading cannon. Both of these were dependent upon Krupp steel.

The well-tuned Prussian military machine was, on a pretext, set in action by Bismarck against the country that had been his ally in the Danish campaign – Austria.

In six weeks the war was over. Prussia's crushing victory guaranteed it the leadership of the North German Confederation and added four million people to her population, with an added bonus of two army corps.

Krupp's reputation was enhanced by the brilliant performance of his guns. His immediate reward was a new steelmaking process that would tide him over his problems with the Bessemer converter. Six scientifically gifted brothers, the Siemens, were spreading their inventive talents across Europe. Werner, the eldest, had set up a multinational electrical firm in Germany, while Karl Wilhelm, now a naturalized Englishman and later to be knighted as Sir William Siemens, had developed an alternative to the Bessemer process for making steel. This *open-hearth process* he now offered to Alfred as 'our leading industrialist', suggesting where his true national loyalties lay.

Siemens's idea with the open-hearth was quite an old one. The problem was to reach the high furnace temperatures needed to melt the steel and separate it from the slag. Siemens's answer was to use the heat in the outgoing gases to warm up the incoming gas that was the fuel for the furnace. Instead of filling a tall converter with complicated air-pipes, the white-hot metal simply lay in a shallow hearth. Although this was slower, it was simpler and cheaper and could cheerfully accept up to half its load in the form of scrap steel.

With refractory linings designed by the French ironmasters, Pierre and Etienne Martin, the Siemens-Martin open-hearth furnace produced good steel from higher phosphorus ores than the Bessemers could handle. But neither process was suitable for the prolific, very high-phosphorus ores, and the rapid development of the steel industry met a sudden pause. Again the professionals provided no solution, and progress had to await a discovery by a young police-court clerk who was also an amateur scientist.

In the year 1867, however, the Siemens process came as a godsend to Krupp. Napoleon III was getting seriously concerned about the growing strength of Prussia: if only he could be converted to the use of steel cannon he would become a most valuable customer. What with the demands for steel for armaments and the insatiable world-wide appetite for steel railway tyres, Krupp was in need of all the steelmaking capacity he could get. Yet this dynamic expansion was bringing its own difficulties. He had to withstand accusations of selling to potential enemies of Prussia the very cannon which might one day be turned round to kill Prussian soldiers. His answer was always that he had not sold any such cannon. It was true that he had not done so; but it was certainly not for the lack of trying.

Undeterred by rebuffs in the international arms trade that he was so anxious to promote, he dashed off to the Paris Exhibition of 1868. As usual he mounted an eye-catching display, including a 40 tonne ingot of steel and a gigantic 30 centimetre cannon. The barrel alone weighed 50 tonnes, and the carriage was another 40.

When Krupp was given the award of officer's rank in the Legion of Honour by a suitably impressed Napoleon III, he chose the moment to pop the question: would his most gracious Majesty care to place an order for some of his fine steel cannon?

Thanks to some swift staffwork by Krupp's French rivals, the Schneiders, the proposition was blocked. But the very fact that the proposal was made, at a time when Franco-Prussian relations were at flashpoint, shows the strength of the world's leading gunsmith and steelmaker. What would the other Prussian gods make of it? To Alfred's horror he learned that both Wilhelm and Bismarck had already attended the firing trials of some 22 centimetre cannon supplied by that upstart British armament manufacturer and would-be Krupp, Mr W. G. Armstrong. Outraged (even though he was at that moment sitting in Moscow signing huge gun contracts with the

Czar), he announced that it was a matter of honour that the Royal Prussian Navy should buys its guns at home.

Coolly he collected a statement from the Russian admirals preferring his cannon to Armstrong's and recommending Wilhelm to stay with Krupps, the very best. The King accepted this astonishing advice from a bunch of foreign admirals, and Armstrong abandoned his attempts to sell guns to Prussia. He retreated instead into a fruitful alliance with the other British arms and steel manufacturer, Vickers. Tom Vickers had begun in the lucrative steel railway tyre business, and he had used the profits to work his way into guns. In 1927 the two associates would merge into one: Vickers-Armstrong Ltd.

Two years after the Paris Exhibition, on 30 June 1870, the French Prime Minister proclaimed that 'the peace of Europe seems better assured than at any previous period'. A fortnight later his cabinet announced general mobilization. In the middle of a diplomatic dispute about who should accept the Spanish throne, Bismarck had managed to re-word a telegram from the King in such a way that it was read as an insult to Napoleon III. War was, as he had planned, inevitable. Napoleon was also eager for a conflict, and he immediately took up the challenge. On 2 August, six French divisions crossed the border heading for the west bank of the Rhine and drove the Prussians out of Saarbrucken.

The outside world looked to a quick victory by the French who were the clear favourites. *The Times* thought that its readers would be well advised to lay their 'last shilling on Casquette against Pumpernickel'. A few looked beyond the sounds of battle to the tragedy behind it. Kate Amberly, soon to give birth to the future philosopher and nuclear disarmer Bertrand Russell, wrote with patrician detachment: 'It makes one miserable to think of that lovely Rhine a seat of war.'

The French command was in no doubt of the result. They issued the army with very good maps of Germany but not a single map of France. They hastily published a French-German dictionary to be in time for use when they reached Berlin. The army was equipped with the new Chassepot, a breech-loading rifle and a primitive form of machine gun, the Mitrailleuse, which could fire 150 rounds a minute. But in two other matters they turned out to be fatally deficient: railways and steel cannon.

The French railway organization was so inept that a fortnight after mobilization had started only half of the 400 000 men who should then have been at the frontier had arrived. And even they had not received their ammunition because the trains were too busy shunting the remaining soldiers to and fro in search of their correct destinations.

The French field guns were made of bronze. They were heavy, inaccurate, and lacking in range. Krupp's high-velocity steel cannon had been rejected, and Schneiders had chosen to ignore the British technique of reinforcing their wrought-iron barrels with exterior coils of wire. Napoleon might have done better if, as William Manchester pointed out, before rejecting Krupp's steel guns he had read the recent novel of one of his own subjects, Jules Verne. In *Twenty Thousand Leagues under the Sea*, Captain Nemo tells a visitor to his submarine, the *Nautilus*, that the engines are made from 'the finest steel in the world, cast by Krupp in Prussia'.

By September the onslaught of Krupp steel had proved decisive. Napoleon III, together with 84 000 soldiers, 2700 officers and 39 generals, surrendered after a debacle near Sedan and France, the proud and confident country of France, was beaten. Paris, however, was not.

SEVEN

The Ring of Steel

Brothers of Germany! Once more, on the pretext of European equilibrium, of national honour, the peace of the world is menaced by political ambitions. French, German, Spanish workers! Let our voices unite in one cry of reprobation against war! . . .

In answer to the warlike proclamations of those who exempt themselves from the impost of blood, and find in public misfortunes a source of fresh speculations, we protest, we who want peace, labour and liberty! . . .

Reveil, 15 July 1870

As Charles Taine hurried through the narrow lanes of Montparnasse there was an electric tension in the air. A summer thunderstorm had almost washed out yesterday's Bastille celebrations, but the strange sensation had nothing to do with the weather. That humid July day in 1870 was one of those rare moments when the future of a nation, a continent, perhaps even a world, hung in the balance. This was not perceived by those who were directly involved. They felt an excitement in the bones, a tingling of the skin, but the only conscious effect was to heighten everyday events and magnify their seeming importance. Charles was worrying about the orders at the printery. Would they still keep going? What if it was found that he and his brother had printed the anti-royalist pamphlets going around during the revels? What news would his friend Maurice bring back from Berlin and London? And, the most pressing anxiety of all, how were they going to manage now that Danielle was again pregnant?

The questions raced around his mind as he crossed into the road along the bank of the Seine. The fresh, misty smell rising from the river and the pink glow of dawn on the towers of Notre Dame flooded into boyhood memories of picnics in the woods and great dishes of strawberries and cream. He and Danielle had been dreaming of such picnics to come with their little son Pascal. Now there was to be another to join them.

Such musings swept abruptly from his mind as he turned up the hill towards the printery and found a column of Mobile Guardsmen bearing down on him. There was just time to jump into a doorway and watch them galloping by. A fit of coughing shook his thin frame. Damn their souls, he swore, not content with parading up and down all yesterday they've got to be out at dawn to keep the war fever going.

In the printery his brother Denis was already working at his press, arguing furiously over his shoulder with the young apprentice. 'Honour?', he asked, 'what honour has our Emperor ever had? Enough to send thousands of young boys to their deaths. And now he's at it again; and just because his precious ambassador has been rejected by the King of Prussia you think? No, he's marching off to the Rhine because he *needs* a war to take people's minds away from the rottenness and corruption he's got the country into. He'll go ahead, no matter how many Frenchmen have to die.'

Charles Taine entered the room, bending his head to miss the oak beam over the door. Still out of breath, he perched on the corner of a bench, his opening words freezing what might have been left of the conversation. 'They're voting this afternoon on the army subsidy for the war,' he told them. 'Jules Favre is going to oppose it. He still believes that the whole thing is a trick to drive the stock market up and make a few more fortunes.'

'He says he does,' chimed in the apprentice. 'More likely he's trying to drive it down again and make a bit for himself.'

'So young and so cynical?', mocked Denis. 'I suppose reading the newspapers is enough to make anyone cynical. All screaming for death or glory.' He handed Charles a copy of the daily *Reveil* with an article ringed in red crayon. 'You won't have seen this yet.'

Charles skimmed through the article and looked up with a wry smile. 'Noble, but hopeful. From what I saw yesterday most people are eager to go. Perhaps the Prussians are different, but I expect that they'll also be happy to march off and die for the honour of their precious King and country. We'll know more about that when Maurice Dupont gets here.'

It might have surprised him to learn that one Prussian who was decidely unhappy at the prospect of war was Herr Alfred Krupp.

Two months earlier Krupp had laid the foundation stone for what was to be a monument to his family name and to himself. The Pharaohs had their pyramids and the tradition would run right through to Randolph Hearst with his castle of San Simeon (or, if you prefer, Citizen Kane with his Xanadu). Now Alfred Krupp was creating his own castle in Essen, *der Villa Hügel*, the house on the hill.

It was a masterpiece of eccentricity. For five years he had laboured on the drawings, trusting to no architect and so being free to pander to his neuroses. He was afraid of fire, so wood was out; construction must be confined to steel and stone. Gas was too dangerous to contemplate; lighting must be entirely by candles. There would be 200 rooms in the main part of the house, including a suite on the second floor that would be permanently reserved for the King. To prevent draughts all windows would be sealed. And to profit from his belief in the health-giving properties of the smell of horse manure, he had his own study built directly over the stables.

So why, in this third week of July 1870, with a profitable war looming up that would devour guns and shells, was Alfred Krupp so depressed? It was because the beautiful limestone he had chosen for his house could only be obtained from the quarry at Chantilly; and that, most regrettably, was located 40 kilometres to the north of Paris.

By the end of the week, when France declared war on Prussia, Charles Taine's cynicism and Alfred Krupp's pessimism seemed to be justified. Flags flew and bells rang in Berlin and Paris. In both cities crowds chanted war songs and packed the churches to pray for victory. *Le Figaro* opened a fund to give every French soldier a cigar and a glass of brandy. The entire student body of the Prussian university of Bonn joined up. In the first skirmish of the war a French general was killed by a Krupp shell. It was a portent.

Six weeks later, Louis Napoleon was riding desperately across the battlefields of Sedan. In crippling agony from a kidney stone, he was hoping for the shot that would bring him at least a hero's death. Even in this he failed. His Prussian captors permitted him to send a bitter telegram to the Empress Eugenie in Paris: 'The army is defeated.'

Bismarck demanded not only the Emperor but also the entire French force as prisoners of war. Reluctantly his demand was accepted, but only after General von Moltke displayed his map of Sedan showing the French positions encircled by a ring of 500 Krupp steel cannon.

These fearful guns had devastated the French army as it lay trapped between the little town of Sedan and the river Meuse. Heroic French cavalry charges were made repeatedly, but all came to grief on the tortured and broken ground that remained after the shelling. In the carnage, 17 000 Frenchmen lay dead or dying with their horses; honour, however, was saved. The Prussians, who had lost only 9000 men, accepted the surrender of the remaining 80 000 French, but allowed the officers to retain the symbols of their class and their manhood, their steel swords.

Early in the morning of 4 September 1870, the news of Louis Napoleon's surrender spread through Paris. Denis and Charles Taine left the printery to join the angry crowds that were milling through the streets, taking Denis's wife Martine with them. She and her sister had been taking turns in the work ever since the young apprentice, despite much sarcasm from Denis, had gone off to join the colours.

They worked their way down to the river bank in the hope of getting to the Bourbon Palace, but the crush was impossible. After much struggling they found themselves in the vast Place de la Concorde, where everybody seemed to be shouting, waving their arms, or standing on a box trying to address anyone who was willing to listen.

Wild rumours passed from neighbour to neighbour, but soon one rumour rose about the rest. It appeared that the crowd outside the Bourbon had forced its way inside. There and then they had compelled the assembled Chamber of Deputies to set up a new government, the Government of the Third Republic. An election of ministers was even now taking place. The Empire was finished. The Empress Eugenie, with her various alleged lovers, and the Crown Prince, had fled to England. All over the square you could hear laughing and cheering.

When it seemed likely that this rumour was accurate, Martine and Charles went back to get the printery ready for action; Denis was left to work his way as near to the palace as he could to glean the full story.

The full story could not, of course, be gleaned by Denis or by anyone else, then or since. But through the fog surrounding those events certain things seem to be clear. Urged on by the strident demands of the crowd packing the Palais Bourbon, the Deputies proclaimed a Government of National Defence. The military governor of Paris, General Trochu, was to be President and Leon Gambetta Minister of the Interior. Hopes of victory again surged high; it was not realized that General Trochu had no faith in the ability of Paris to defend itself and was simply playing for time to obtain better terms when the ultimate capitulation took place.

Time was running out. A fortnight later two Prussian cavalry patrols met at St Germain, and Paris was encircled. Throughout autumn and into an exceptionally cruel winter, the ring of steel around the city stayed in place; the Prussians were not strong enough to break through the fortifications, and the Parisians were not strong enough to break out. Von Moltke was content to maintain the siege, confident that the hunger and suffering of the trapped population would soon lead them to surrender.

One warm October night, the gallant minister, Gambetta, sailed out over the Prussian lines in a coal-gas balloon. Landing in Tours, 100 kilometres to the south-west, he raised huge armies which engaged the Prussians in bloody battles for the next three months. They were unsuccessful. Paris remained besieged, and the morale of the ordinary Parisians began to sink; they were now counting themselves lucky when they were able to dine on horse or rat. But the morale of the quarter of a million Prussians camped outside, and of their families at home, was also sinking. On Thursday, 5 January 1871, Bismarck decided that the pressure had become unbearable. He could wait no longer. The time had come to use his secret weapon, the bombardment of Paris, the City of Light.

Krupp gun preparing to bombard Paris, 1871

EIGHT

An Incident

The great questions of the day will not be settled by resolutions and majority votes but by iron and blood.

Otto von Bismarck

As the pale light of dawn begins to fill the Parisian sky a gaunt young bookbinder is walking quickly away from a wall poster still dripping with paste. TO THE PEOPLE OF PARIS! shouts the poster, so loudly that he feels that every gendarme on the Left Bank must hear it and come running. If they do, and if they read that fervent appeal to the people of Paris:

DOWN WITH THE USELESS GOVERNMENT!

JOIN THE COMMUNE!

UNITE TO DRIVE OUT THE PRUSSIAN INVADERS!

that will be the end of Charles Taine.

7 AM, Thursday, 5 January 1871

Charles crosses the road; he is walking more slowly now, but he soon reaches his tenement in the rue Lalande. As he is entering, he hears the shrill cry of a new born baby, sharp enough to bring a temporary halt to the background whispering of the rats.

He bounds up the stairs two at a time and rushes to the side of his exhausted wife Danielle. In their only armchair her sister is sponging the new infant and wrapping her tenderly in the length of soft, fine cloth that Charles brought home from the printery. Joyful, yet anxious, he strokes the mother's hair and gazes through the tiny window at the dawn. What can the future hold for his little piece of humanity? For three months they have been living inside that surrounding trap of steel and, at any time, it may start to close . . .

8 AM, 5 January 1871

In the study in Rothschild's chateau at Versailles, 20 kilometres west of the rue Lalande, the Iron Chancellor Otto von Bismarck is dictating letters to his secretaries. 'Paris has not yet yielded, though it is close to starvation,' he writes. 'Our troops cannot endure the cold and the disease much longer. But there is agitation among the French workers. An insurrection may yet save us from the carnage of a direct assault upon the city.'

As he is dwelling on the consequences of the French political infighting, his dictation is cut short by a clatter of horses' hooves on the drive outside the huge bay window. An out-of-breath staff officer in field grey enters with a brief message: 'Marshal von Moltke wishes you to know that the big Krupp cannons are now in position and ready to fire.'

'God be thanked,' murmurs the Iron Chancellor, half to himself. 'Then let them begin . . .'

8.30 AM, 5 January 1871

In Berlin the morning papers are screaming for action. They adorn their front pages with the popular ditty:

> Good von Moltke don't be dumb,
> End it quickly: Bumm! Bumm! Bumm!

9 AM, 5 January 1871

Far from Paris or Berlin, beyond the source of the Rhine but still within earshot of the distant guns, Richard Wagner stretches himself drowsily inside his silken sheets. Recalling the end of his dream he sits up abruptly, lights the candle and picks up the unfinished score he is working on. His fearless hero Siegfried bursts through the ring of fire to win the fair maiden. In his hand is Nothung, his invincible sword of steel. The steel sword is the symbol of potency, of military power, that has lived in legend since the days when the men of the Iron Age were vanquishing the men of the Bronze. Siegfried has used the sword to defeat the god who tried to bar his way and now, Wagner muses, to the most stirring music ever heard, he will penetrate the fiery ring and claim his prize.

9.30 AM, 5 January 1871

Sir Charles Monckton-Smith sits down at his breakfast table and opens his neatly folded copy of *The Times*. The latest report from

William Russell in Paris greets him: 'In Strasbourg, as a result of the siege, a hospital for children who have lost limbs has had to be established.'

10 AM, 5 January 1871
'Elevation thirty degrees!'
'Elevation thirty degrees.'
'Range 7000 metres!' said the Prussian gunlayer in charge of the huge Krupp cannon, with just a momentary pause. If the gun could throw its 50 kilogram missile through that distance, a full kilometre more than it had ever travelled on the range, it would burst somewhere down on the Left Bank of the Seine, right in the heart of Paris . . .

10.05 AM, 5 January 1871
Charles Taine has been to the printery and is hurrying home with a rare gift for his family – a package of fruit and cakes, some real mutton and a small bottle of milk. As he is crossing the street into the rue Lalande, a whistling sound overhead ends in a deafening explosion and, as the smoke clears, the torn body of Charles Taine lies sprawled across the pavement. His chest has been torn by a jagged fragment of steel, and his blood is flowing on the cobblestones . . .

NINE

The Commune

Vivre Libre, ou Mourir!

Paris Commune Poster, 4 September, 1870

The Prussian gunners fired their initial salvos on that cold January morning in 1871 so that they could check the range. Sightings from suitable vantage points confirmed their accuracy and over the next three weeks several thousand shells were fired into Paris. The explosions caused much damage to property but only a few hundred human casualties. As a consequence the property owners were strengthened in their desire to conclude an armistice and the common people were strengthened in their resolve to continue the fight. One woman was overheard saying to her child, 'If you don't behave yourself I won't take you to see the bombardment.'

Bismarck was triumphant. Just as he had hoped, politics were dividing the French against each other and the Prussians would be spared from making a frontal attack on Paris. On 18 January he arranged for Wilhelm to be crowned Emperor of Germany in the Hall of Mirrors at Versailles. At last the German states were unified, and now they were settling the questions of the day by his policy of blood and iron. Ten days later the French government signed the armistice.

Denis Taine came storming into the printery in a foul mood. 'God damn them,' he growled, 'the billion francs don't really matter, but why give away Alsace and half Lorraine as well? With half a million National Guard here the Prussians could never have taken Paris. And they couldn't last much longer out there anyway; one more sortie and we would have broken through to join up with the armies in the provinces.'

'Just listen to the great pacifist talking,' replied Martine. 'I thought you said the National Guard was a bunch of irresponsible radicals; except for poor Charles, I suppose, and a few of your cronies.'

A lame apprentice who had been excused from duty with the National Guard saw that as his cue to join in. He reminded them that they had all been against the war at the start. But that was when the King of Prussia had announced that he was only fighting a 'defensive' war. Now that he'd become Emperor of Germany it was a different story, wasn't it? Turning to the tall young man who had been quietly stacking reams of paper on a bench in the corner, he asked, 'And what do you make of it all?'

Maurice Dupont thought the most important thing just then was to stop a war from breaking out inside the printery. He'd returned from Berlin and London four months ago, just before the gates into Paris were closed. Since then there'd been precious little chance to pursue his efforts to organize a union. He tried briefly to answer the apprentice's question. 'I've talked to many people while I've been away, and I can assure you that there's plenty of international support for the defenders of Paris. But there's no chance of that support taking a military form; certainly not after the performance of the Prussian army. If anything is to be done Paris will have to do it alone.

Isle of the Pines, Noumea. The tropical fortress where the exiled Communards were imprisoned

And from the way the organizers of the National Guard are shaping up I think it's likely that something will be done, despite the armistice signed by that traitor Adolphe Thiers.'

For the moment, however, there was work to be done, books to be bound, the latest government posters on food rationing to be printed. Martine wanted to finish early. She had promised to help Danielle and the children in the apartment upstairs where they had been living with her and Denis since Charles's death. Maurice Dupont worked in the printery whenever he had a spare hour or two. He agreed to take over for a while from Martine, but before doing so he wanted them to hear his answer to the apprentice's question.

'It's important,' he told them, 'to remember just who are our enemies and who are our friends. It seems hard to say so, but those spike-helmeted Prussian soldiers are no more the enemy than our own gallant lads who marched into Prussia six months ago. Our real enemies are the same as they always were, the cold-hearted men of power, the Bismarcks and the Thiers, and the men who make the guns for them, the Schneiders and the Krupps. Those are the people whom in the end we'll have to beat.'

As he spoke of the need to preserve our comradeship with the people of Berlin, he was thinking wistfully of Lise and his promise to return. Unusually for him, he managed to finish his speech without becoming heated, and the little printery got down again to the work of the day.

For the next two months it was hard enough to preserve body and soul in the poorer districts of Paris. The new National Assembly, set up provocatively 15 kilometres away from the city in Versailles, was slowly tightening the screws on the capital. It tightened them just too far. Thiers's first mistake was to declare that all outstanding debts must be repaid immediately. It was a decision that appealed greatly to the property owners of the Assembly and to the financiers but hardly at all to the shopkeepers and small business people, many of whom it ruined.

A still greater blunder was to send troops into Paris to commandeer the artillery of the National Guard, overlooking the fact that the guardsmen had actually paid for most of it themselves. Frustrated by the refusal of the guardsmen to hand over their guns, Thiers's officers lost their nerve. On the night of 18 March, General Lecomte ordered the men of his 81st regiment to fire on an unarmed gathering in the Place Pigalle. When they refused, he insulted them angrily and repeated his order. The soldiers raised their rifles and shot the general instead. The civil war had begun.

'Civil war be damned!' cursed Denis to the grocer, sipping a glass of watery wine with him in the bistro. 'This is no civil war. It's two gangs of brigands attacking the people of Paris. Why do you think Thiers has fled to Versailles? Because he likes the gardens? And why is Bismarck sending 10 000 prisoners of war back to him at this very moment? So that he can suppress us, that's why. They're both more afraid of us than ever they were of each other.'

'If you're right,' objected the grocer, 'we might as well give in now. We can't fight the French and the German armies as well. That's why I'm going to vote for the moderates; they'll try for a compromise settlement. Those crazy revolutionary extremists frighten me to death. If they got control we'd be slaughtered.'

Moderates there were among the successful candidates, but overwhelmed by the size of the radical majority they at once resigned. The new council turned for its inspiration to the Paris Commune that saved the republic during the French Revolution. It proclaimed itself a new Commune; it would govern Paris and save the republic once again.

The printery was now in a flurry of activity. Government proclamations were coming out daily, on everything from art exhibitions to public conveniences. Young boys and girls were recruited to help get through the work.

At the end of March, Louise Michel had come in to have two orders printed. One abolished the control of public prostitutes by the police; the other granted the pension to illegitimate dependants of National Guards. Louise Michel was already notorious among the supporters of Thiers who called her 'The Red Virgin of Montmartre', evidently the worst thing they could think of. The illegitimate daughter of an aristocrat, she had been a poet and a teacher before the war, and was now an organizer of the Women's Battalion for the defence of Paris. Soon after her visit, Martine and Danielle announced that they would be spending some time each day training with the battalion.

And still the proclamations poured in. Pawnshops were prevented from selling the goods they were holding for their customers. House rents were controlled. Thiers's law requiring immediate payment of debts and loans was cancelled. As a start on education reform, compulsory religion was removed, and all materials such as pens, paper, books and maps had to be issued free of charge. Night work by bakers was abolished. As a gesture against militarism the 50 metre high Vendôme column, topped by a triumphal bronze statue of Napoleon I, was demolished in a great public ceremony and the guillotine was burned.

Four hundred proclamations were issued in nine weeks, a frenzy of social reform carried out in the middle of war. It was as though the Commune leaders knew that was all the time they would have.

In one of the most cynical deals of the century, Thiers's troops at Versailles were reinforced by French prisoners of war, released by Bismarck for the express purpose of crushing the Commune. In April they launched their first attacks on Paris. They captured a number of prisoners and set the tone for the fighting that was to follow by shooting many of them on the spot. As the weeks passed they moved their positions closer and closer, while the Parisians still seemed more concerned with social reforms, theatres and concerts than with actively prosecuting the war. They didn't seem to realize that with two armies now surrounding them, they also had enemies within the gates.

In the middle of May Denis arrived back at the printery to find it gutted by fire. With a shock he saw that the staircase was a charred wreck, but he soon found out that Martine, Danielle and the children were safe and in a house across the street. One of the recent employees was missing. He had been suspected of monarchist sympathies and the last anti-clerical proclamation had been too much for him. He must have come in early that morning and started the fire, probably with paraffin and some oily rags; it would have been easy enough.

This small piece of sabotage was a foretaste of events to come on Sunday. A supporter of the Versailles junta discovered that the Point-du-Jour gate in the western districts of the city was for a time left completely unguarded and signalled the news from the wall. By nightfall 70 000 of the French troops had poured into the city.

The week that followed was violent and nightmarish. Slowly but mercilessly the Versailles troops fought their way across towards the eastern bounds of the city, firing their cannon down each street into the barricades hastily thrown up by the guard. Some of the communards sailed gunboats down the Seine and bombarded the invading troops; others set fire to buildings in their path, a scorched earth policy of defiance rather than surrender.

All attempts to get the printery back into working order had been abandoned. The remaining apprentices were fighting side by side with Denis in the local brigade. Martine and Danielle had taken the children to stay with Maurice Dupont's mother in Belleville, which was on the side of Paris farthest from the breakthrough. Martine had gone to join Louise Michel's battalion in the thick of the action, and Maurice had disappeared, muttering about getting the women out through the German lines.

By Sunday morning most of the city had fallen to the invaders. Ancient houses, ministries and palaces were aflame, and a pall of smoke blotted out the blue skies of a beautiful spring morning. Processions of prisoners – men, women, and children – were hurried along by the soldiers on their way to Versailles and, in many cases, to death.

The despairing communards fought savagely and often heroically. Deciding that all was lost, the Jacobin leader Louis Delescluze dressed up in his 1848 parliamentary costume – top hat, frock coat and the broad red sash of the Commune – mounted the barricade at the Château d'Eau and brandished his cane defiantly at the enemy until they shot him dead.

Belleville had fallen. Its streets were littered with broken barricades and the bodies of the dead and dying. The Belleville guard was still making a last stand, gravestone by gravestone, in the ancient cemetery of Père-Lachaise. Miraculously neither Danielle and her children nor Madame Dupont had been at home when the conquerors arrived. Maurice had turned up with a horse and cart and taken them off through one of the northern gates where, he had discovered, Saxon soldiers were turning a blind eye to the passage of refugees. By Sunday night, Paris had fallen, but they were far away on the road to the north.

Among the 40 000 prisoners crammed into the compounds of Versailles were two who would have dearly loved to have known of the progress of that horse and cart. They did not even know that each had survived. Martine Taine had surrendered with the remnants of the women's battalion. The women were convicted of setting fire to buildings, and some were condemned to death. Despite her fervent appeal to be allowed to die with the others, Louise Michel was sentenced to life imprisonment on the Pacific island of New Caledonia. So was her friend Martine Taine.

Denis Taine would also have wanted to know of the escaping

horse and cart had he been sufficiently conscious. His left arm had been blown off by an exploding shell on the barricades. Tended by his fellow guardsmen, he had reached Versailles more dead than alive, and he was barely surviving in the primitive hospital that had been rigged up for the prisoners. It was months before he was fit enough to stand trial, but even then he had two more years to wait in prison before the overloaded courts could deal with him. The harshness of the early days had softened, the occupying troops had departed, the investment climate had improved, and the magisterial classes were facing life with renewed confidence. They were condescendingly lenient to the one-armed Denis, giving him five years' hard labour and a fine of 1000 francs. The Taines and the Duponts were down but not out.

Commune recruiting poster: 1870

TEN

Mr Thomas's Discovery

Fortune favours the prepared mind.

Louis Pasteur

Europe woke up on the Monday morning after the death of the Commune, shook off the hung-over feeling from its nightmare and got down to work. The French had to get their economy going again in spite of the vast bill for reparations and the loss of Alsace-Lorraine. Bismarck was welding together the new state of Germany with the aim of making it the most powerful in the world. Britain, already the workshop of the world, was just beginning to look apprehensively over its shoulder at its rivals in Germany and the United States of America who were threatening to overtake her. Already the rising tide of industrialization was pushing up the demand for steel.

Alfred Krupp, however, was less happy than he should have been. The fourteen-year-old boy with his seven workmen half a century ago had grown into Germany's leading industrialist, employing 10 000. In the war his steel guns had done all that anyone asked of them; indeed, more. True, some of their breech mechanisms had burst, with unfortunate effects on the gunners, but new orders were rolling in from round the world. Better still, his stone slabs for the Villa Hügel would be coming through unimpeded now that Paris had fallen. No longer would he have to go on paying the exorbitant costs of the loads smuggled out during the siege. What could be troubling him now?

Cannon King Alfred was worried about his steel. Of course, he would now get as much iron ore as he wanted from the mines of Lorraine, but did he really want it? The damned stuff was full of phosphorus, and he was having enough trouble with phosphorus in his Bessemer converters. Even the new open-hearth furnaces that

Siemens had designed for him couldn't handle it. Nobody knew what to do. But there was that fellow at the University of Berlin, the one who had invented their best flux and who was the leading expert on heat treatment. Schiller, Dr Heinz Schiller.

So it was that Alfred Krupp took the train to Berlin in the summer of 1871. The Military Academy he would certainly visit; and there would be an audience with His Royal Highness, if it could be arranged. But his one fixed appointment was for dinner at No. 157, Friedrichstrasse, the home of the eminent Dr Schiller.

Dinner had been dull; very polite and formal. Frau Schiller, a delicate, rather nervous woman, had introduced her son Kurt and her shy daughter Ilse, and apologized for the absence of her elder daughter Lise who was in England, completing her education.

Under the influence of the wine and in the presence of his distinguished guest, Schiller was becoming expansive. 'She's been sent abroad,' he chimed in, oblivious of his wife's warning look. 'That little monkey needed a change of scene. Last year we heard that she'd been speaking out publicly against the war. A year or two in London with the right people will soon straighten her out,' he declared.

When young Kurt and the women had left them, Krupp came straight to the point. 'Phosphorus is ruin,' he said. 'The only time that our guns ever burst was when the steel was weakened by too much phosphorus. Here we have a wonderful source of cheap ore won for us in Lorraine by our army and it turns out to be loaded with phosphorus. Can you tell me how to get rid of it?'

The metallurgist spoke learnedly for a quarter of an hour, but the answer, as Krupp soon discerned, was going to be no.

This was a problem, he pointed out, that Bessemer had tackled, without success. Warming to his subject he explained that, in the hot converter, high-phosphorus ores combined with oxygen to form phosphoric acid. The acid was the cause of the trouble. It could not combine with the acidic slag already forming in the converter so it went instead into the steel. To a chemist the obvious solution was to add lime.. This would combine with the phosphoric acid and the compound would go into the slag and be separated from the liquid metal in the normal way. But the chemical nature of the slag would have been changed from acidic to basic. At the high temperature of molten steel this *basic slag* would destroy the sandstone lining of the converter. The idea of neutralizing the phosphorus was good in theory but useless in practice.

Thank you for nothing, Krupp thought, but quickly pulled himself together. 'An interesting analysis,' he complimented Schiller, 'but might some basic materials other than lime be suitable? Some other compound that would unite with the phosphorus and enable it to be removed with the slag?'

To add point to these questions, Krupp asked whether the good doctor had all the equipment that he wanted. How did he fare for assistants? Was there anything else that might be of use to him? It was agreed that a visit or two by Dr Schiller to London would not be amiss; quite apart from any technical information he might glean, he would be able to keep a fatherly eye on his wayward daughter.

It was a wise decision. London was an exciting capital, still at the centre of world commerce and industry. Its West End glittered with handsome shops, hotels and theatres, contrasting with the dark factories and dingy housing of its eastern suburbs. In one of those suburbs, Islington, Danielle Taine was putting her children to bed after a tiring afternoon at the zoo. Maurice Dupont was writing a long letter to a friend in Berlin, explaining how, after escaping from Paris, they had decided to go to England. Friends in the union had come to their aid and had found him a job with a publisher.

The person he was writing to in Berlin was at that moment, however, sitting on a stool at a coffee stall in the neighbouring borough of Holborn.

Lise Schiller was feeling very pleased with herself. She had at last persuaded the earnest young man beside her not only to stay behind after the lecture but to crash through his conventionality and let her buy him a cup of coffee and a bun. Despite appearances, she thought, Sidney Gilchrist Thomas was more than your ordinary young Londoner. He worked hard during the day as a police court clerk in the docklands but still found enough energy to walk 15 kilometres each evening for his scientific studies at Birkbeck College. They had met in the advanced chemistry class and this gave them much to talk about. On this occasion they were both sparked off by the challenging lecture they had just heard on the chemistry of steel.

'Don't you think he was exaggerating?' the young man mused. 'It sounds simple enough to make steel from a high-phosphorus ore. Who's going to give you a fortune for solving that one?'

'First solve the problem', laughed Lise, 'then we'll find someone to give you a fortune for it. There'll be plenty of takers in France and Germany.'

'If only we could find something to add, instead of the lime, that would combine with the phosphorus without attacking the sandstone of the converter linings,' mused the young man. 'Isn't there another metal that would take it up more strongly than the steel? I suppose everything like that has already been tried,' he added.

Lise nodded. 'You can count on that,' she assured him. 'They'll have tried everything from chalk to turnip tops. I bet they haven't thought of using these buns, though; one of them would suck the phosphorus out of a stone. But perhaps we'd do better to hunt for quite a different kind of lining for the converter. It could be made from a basic material, not like the acid sandstone, so that it wouldn't react and fall to bits when the lime is put in to bind the phosphorus. It's also got to be tough to stand up to a temperature of more than 1500 degrees!'

Sidney Thomas looked up. 'The kind of thing they use for molten glass?' he offered. 'Do you remember those lectures last term on glassmaking?'

Lise remembered them very well. They had reminded her of a holiday she'd once spent in the Tyrol. On their way there the Schillers had stayed overnight in a small town near the Swiss border and her father, as usual, had seized every chance to promote his children's education. The next day they visited a farm, a watchmaker's establishment, and a small glassworks. The glassmaker was experimenting with different linings for his vats, building them up in layers with a paste made from the local stone. She had been struck by its name – dolomite – because that was the name of the mountains they were on their way to climb, the Dolomites. It was a chalky sort of stone, a mixture of calcium and magnesium carbonate.

Perhaps something like that might do for the steel furnaces. A paste made from a powdered basic rock. But what liquid had the glassmaker used to bind the paste together? Ah, that she couldn't remember. She hadn't noticed the liquid. Never mind, there was plenty of time to try all the powders and liquids they could think of. Life was long, and at that moment life was sweet. Even Sidney had to laugh at her exotic suggestions.

'I've got an idea for the binding liquid,' he started to say, but he was cut off by a yelp from Lise.

'Look!', she cried, pointing to a pattern on the wooden boards at the back of the stall, 'it's moving.' Sidney peered closely and realized that the 'pattern' was a gathering of cockroaches, actually looking quite artistic in the greenish glare of the acetylene gas lamps. They decided it was time to go.

Sidney and Lise talked for a little while before parting, she to return to the house of her father's friends in Bloomsbury, he to start the long walk home to Canonbury.

And so it was that when Dr Schiller visited his daughter in the Christmas holidays, he discovered from his solicitous enquiries that she had been having interesting discussions about basic furnace linings, but he never knew that only some cockroaches in a London coffee stall had prevented him from discovering Sidney Gilchrist Thomas's solution to the most vital steel problem of the time.

ELEVEN

The Master of Iron

CUSINS: What on earth is the true faith of an Armourer?
UNDERSHAFT: To give arms to all men who offer an honest price for them, without respect of persons or principles.

George Bernard Shaw, *Major Barbara*

For once Alfred Krupp was happy. Sitting in his cold, candlelit castle, he felt that everything was working out. He no longer had to worry about asphyxiating from his own body fumes, which he was convinced had toxic properties; when he awoke in the night, which was quite often, he would just get up, stroll down one of the long corridors of the Villa Hügel, and go to sleep again in another bedroom. And business was booming. A dozen American railroads were buying his steel tyres, and the United States was already looking like a giant spider's web made from a million tonnes of Krupp steel rails.

Better still, the world was coming to recognize him as its leading armourer. He had confirmed this impression with a master-stroke of showmanship. At his private proving range in Hanover, fully 17 kilometres long, he had successfully conducted his showpiece, the 'Bombardment of the Nations'. Artillery officers of a dozen countries had sipped champagne in luxurious bunkers while they watched targets being demolished by Krupp shells, precisely according to the programme they held in their hands. And in the folder of supporting documents he had included glowing testimonials to the performance of his guns from both sides in the Russian-Turkish war that had just finished in January of that year, 1878. Mentally rubbing his hands together, he estimated that over 20 000 Krupp cannon were facing each other across different frontiers round the world.

Not that he was in favour of war. He wrote to his 12 000 'children', the 'Kruppianer' as he called his employees, saying how dear peace was to his heart. If war came it might mean the end of the steelworks, their jobs, and the houses and social security services he had provided for them. But how was peace to be assured? Only by being strong. The sharper your sword, the less likely you were to be attacked.

It was a convincing argument. It was repeated enthusiastically by Bismarck and it has echoed down the years ever since, muted only during times of warfare that have repeatedly intervened to the temporary loss of its credibility.

So tonight Alfred Krupp was happy, his joy crowned by a letter from his adviser in Berlin, Dr Schiller. Sitting alone in the huge dining hall, at a table 20 metres long, he sipped his wine and carefully re-read the message he had long awaited.

The candles of five chandeliers provided his light. His Bohemian wineglass, specially blown to hold a whole litre, was in perfect harmony with its surroundings and accorded with his doctor's instructions not to take more than one glass of wine a day.

The letter informed Krupp that the young man, Sidney Thomas, had succeeded in overcoming the problem of excessive phosphorus. His method, of which Schiller possessed full details, involved making a refractory lining in the furnace from a paste of powdered dolomite and tar. A layer half a metre thick was built up and rammed solid. Lime was then added to the charge. Although the lining was soon eaten away by the fierce chemical reactions, it was just as easily replaced. Practical tests by Thomas's cousin at a Welsh ironworks had been completely successful. The huge deposits of ore in Lorraine and in Cleveland could now be exploited. This young Englishman had just doubled the steelmaking potential of the world.

Thomas had reported his discovery at the Iron and Steel Institute, but nobody had taken much notice. How like the English, Schiller observed. Hadn't they done the same to Bessemer? Thomas had applied for patents for the process, which could be more serious. In Schiller's opinion, however, it would not pose much of a problem to Krupp's experienced legal department.

That night the lonely old man went to bed in a glow of contentment. The race for world supremacy was on. It was unmistakable. England was faltering; the United States was forging ahead; but no one, not even Bismarck, had done more than Alfred, the nervous youth who had taken over the tiny firm of Friedrich Krupp half a century ago, to ensure that the race would be won by Germany. Blood and iron, that was the key. He had made himself the master of iron. He had forged it into the finest steel in the world, thrown networks of railways over continents, and built the guns which would answer all the questions. He opened a drawer in a bedside cabinet that was stuffed with sashes and medals. Medals from Turkey, Russia, Belgium and Brazil. The Legion of Honour from France and the Sacred Order of Christ (Commander's Cross) from Portugal. A drawer full of tributes to the man who had devoted a lifetime to creating the tightest bond between a steelworks and an army: what an American president would one day call a military-industrial complex. Softly he closed the drawer, snuffed the candles and sank into a blissful sleep.

At that moment, in the Angel Music Hall, Islington, the Great Macdermott was urging the audience to join in his final song. The chorus nearly brought down the rafters:

> We don't want to fight, but by Jingo if we do,
> We've got the ships, we've got the men,
> and we've got the money too!

They knew and loved their Macdermott, had done so ever since he gave them this song. During the Russian-Turkish war it had boosted their spirits when the rumour spread that the Russians were about to take Constantinople. Sending British ironclads through the Dardanelles had frightened away the Russians, but the song had lingered on.

In the gods, Danielle Taine and her sister Françoise were sitting on the hard wooden benches, craning forward for a view of the stage. Françoise had only just arrived in England and she could not understand the song. 'Who is this Jingo they sing about?' she wanted to know. Danielle burst into laughter. 'It is the same as Chauvin', she explained, 'our own belligerent patriot. Jingoism, chauvinism, it's the same thing. But it's a poor sign for the future, isn't it?' she added, as Macdermott was taking his last curtain call. 'Let's have a quick drink with Bill and Harry, and then we can talk some more when we get home.'

Escorted by their two friends, lathe workers at a factory in Clerkenwell, they had threaded their way through the crowds and the hansom cabs clustered round the theatre entrance, down the dimly lit street to the Angel Inn. Sitting inside with their tuppenny glasses of dark, foaming stout, Françoise had launched into a barrage of questions about living conditions in London.

Danielle was enthralled by the conversation. It ranged from the bombardments during the Franco-Prussian war to the Utopia that was on the way because of the marvellous inventions of engineers. How would Françoise have got here fifty years ago, they asked, without any railways? And look how the sewing machine had transformed the lives of women. These were just the beginnings.

The young men were exceptionally proud of the new Sheffield tool steels. The Germans fancied themselves as steelmakers, but what about the fine steel needles they'd presented to Queen Victoria? Almost as fine as a hair, with perfectly formed points and eyes. One needle had been taken to Firth Vickers, in Sheffield, and later returned to the German Embassy. On close inspection the Germans found that a second needle had been hidden inside it. They had no doubts that British engineering was leading the world into a brighter future.

Even Françoise thought that a bit excessive. 'Have you heard of the French businessman Jacob Rothschild,' she enquired. 'Do you know what he said? There are three ways of losing your money: on women, gambling and engineers. The first two are pleasanter, but the last is much the most certain.'

In mock indignation the young men stood up and prepared to escort their companions home. They had hardly left the Angel when they encountered a strange, appetizing aroma. 'That's the latest thing,' Bill told them, 'a fish and chip shop.'

He and Françoise marched off to the shop, but the other two walked on. On the way Danielle talked about engineering and the threat from German industry. She had an uneasy memory of an item in the paper about the world show held recently in Sydney in Australia. The display by Krupps of Essen had been one of the star turns: it had been awarded a gold medal.

Her companion didn't seem to feel at all threatened. He was more interested in the Sunday League, an organization to which you paid a penny a week, and after twelve weeks went on a Sunday railway excursion to the seaside.

But now Danielle must say good night; she had to be up at five for her early morning cleaning job at the clothing factory and after that she would be charring at a big house in Highgate. With this work she could keep the children clothed and fed and help Maurice with the rent.

At No. 157, Friedrichstrasse, Dr Heinz Schiller lingered over his

Sydney Exhibition,

1879.

CAST STEEL MANUFACTORY

OF

FRIED. KRUPP,

NEAR

ESSEN,

Germany.

Trade Mark of the Firm Fried. Krupp.

London:

READ, BROOKS & CO., PRINTERS, 25 & 26. NEW ST., CLOTH FAIR, E.C.

Cover of Krupp catalogue, Sydney, 1879. The exhibits include guns, locomotive axles, springs, wheels, and tyres, all in crucible cast steel, and plates and wheels of iron dinner table, feeling rather pleased with himself. He had got to the bottom of the Thomas process and sent his report to Krupp in Essen. Doubtless he would soon receive some tangible reward for this; the Cannon King had already shown his appreciation of Dr Schiller's efforts, appointing him an official technical adviser, and taking his son Kurt directly into the firm after his graduation. Kurt had done well, though in a way that had surprised his father. Starting off as a qualified scientist in the metallurgical department, he had certainly earned his rapid promotion, but his interest had drifted away from science towards the problems of administering the factory. Last year he had been selected as a personal assistant to Krupp and given the responsibility for communicating Krupp's directives to the workers and for ensuring that they were properly respected.

It was the blunt nature of these directives that surprised Dr Schiller. Everyone knew, of course, that Herr Krupp was the sworn enemy of the social democrats; had he not written to the Kaiser saying that socialism was a serpent at the breast of Germany and must be eliminated whatever the cost?

As the Reichstag elections approached, the directives were made explicit: anyone known to be a social democrat, or who was found doing anything subversive like reading a social democratic newspaper, was to be instantly sacked. All wastepaper baskets in the factory and in the workers' homes would be inspected. And, foreshadowing a wider philosophy that would rule in Germany sixty years later, the workers were told exactly how they should live: by day they should work hard loyally at their allotted jobs, not running around the shop fetching drinks or going to the lavatory without written permission from the foreman. In their homes, enjoying services thoughtfully provided by Krupp, they should concentrate on caring for their families; even at night in their beds they should remember that they were Kruppianer and strive 'to provide the state with plenty of loyal subjects and to develop a special breed of men for the works'.

It was, Dr Schiller had to admit, an effective campaign. Kurt reported that none of the 15 000 workers seemed to object or was observed to smile when handed one of the many directives. Discipline in the works noticeably improved. But when the election results for Essen were announced it was discovered that Alfred Krupp had been defeated by Gerhard Stoetzel, a social democrat who had been a fitter and turner in Krupp's works.

Krupp's fury was matched only by Bismarck's. Although the social democrats held only a few seats in the national Parliament, Bismarck saw them as a threat to German supremacy in the race against England and the United States. His attack on Roman Catholicism was switched to the more immediate enemy, social democracy. Martial law was invoked against any labour unrest, unions were placed under police supervision, and anyone accused of being a socialist ran the risk of being deported.

Dr Schiller was not only happy; he was relieved. Lise had been sent out of sight just in time, and now spent almost as long in England or in Paris as she did at home. There was a battle, however, whenever she and Kurt happened to be in Berlin together which, fortunately, was not very often. Schiller had avoided further trouble by destroying the letters from Lise's dubious associates while she was in England. Krupp must never be reminded that the Schillers harboured a socialist in the family.

Krupp, however, had problems of his own. The workers were not working hard enough, the managers were corrupt and lazy, his servants were incompetent, and he had come to hate his great mausoleum of a house. The brittle façade of his relationship with his wife cracked irrevocably when she left him in 1882. He turned to music for solace. Humperdinck was employed to play for him while he ate his solitary dinner; and he endeavoured to strike up a friendship with Franz Liszt.

All was in vain. He spent his last years designing novel weapons as the last dedication of Krupp steel to the fatherland: armoured guns, a stationary tank, and weapons for the Imperial Navy. One was a floating gun battery of cellular construction, another a naval gun that fired in opposite directions simultaneously to obviate recoil. These were the problems before him when he died, with only his valet in attendance, on Bastille Day in 1887. But the old man's judgement was as sure as ever; Germany's greatest test in the struggle to come would be the battle on the seas. That was where the race would be won or lost.

TWELVE

Death of a Krupp

Whatever happens we have got
The Maxim gun, and they have not.

Hilaire Belloc

William George Armstrong, an English solicitor, loved to walk through the Newcastle docks watching the cranes discharging their loads of coal, glass or manufactured goods into the holds of the great ocean-going freighters or unloading the iron ore that had come across the North Sea from Sweden. One autumn day in 1845, when the cranes seemed to be making particularly hard work of it, puffing and steaming away in the cold November air, Armstrong had a brilliant idea. Why not drive the cranes by hydraulic motors, operated simply by the pressure of the water in the street water mains?

He had always been more interested in science and invention than in the law, and he was quick to seize his chance. Within a few years he had established a successful hydraulic equipment company in Elswick, a village on the outskirts of Newcastle.

The War Office was impressed. When the Crimean War began, they asked him to design submarine mines to blow up Russian ships. Horrified by the crudity of the guns that he found the army using, he set about designing the breech-loading Armstrong gun that revolutionized gun-making and took him irreversibly into the armaments business. Soon after this achievement, he was knighted. When political machinations led to the termination of British orders, he was dismayed, but he decided reluctantly that now he had to sell his weapons abroad. That was how he came to join Krupps of Germany and Schneiders of France as one of the leaders in the international arms race.

The British government was no more worried by Armstrong selling arms abroad than the Kaiser had been by Krupp. When he expanded his activities by building a shipyard for the construction of naval vessels, they elevated him to the peerage. Elswick, meanwhile, was turning into an urban arsenal, its steelworks and gun factories resembling an English version of Essen, and Lord Armstrong, now the world's leading supplier of warships, was starting to show some of the characteristics of a Krupp. A mighty mansion, 'Craigside', was built for him. Here the owner could spend his declining years fulminating against the objectionable behaviour of his workers, still more objectionable now that they were organizing themselves into trade unions.

At 'Craigside', Armstrong was able to indulge in some technical oneupmanship over his German rival in the Villa Hugel. Instead of candles and chandeliers, he installed the new electric lighting, powered from a dynamo driven by a convenient stream. He designed an exotic conservatory in which the plants were hydraulically rotated so that they always faced the sun. But the trimmings could not disguise the eternal philosophy of the armourer. Armstrong claimed that he was merely the servant of those who carried the responsibility for war or peace. In any case, he declared, in a memorable phrase, as time goes on the increasing sophistication of weapons will steadily reduce the barbarity of war.

While England and Germany jockeyed for position, the French were still recovering from the war and its political reactions. But by 1881, a republican government was sitting confidently again in Paris, 'The Marseillaise' had been declared the national song and 14 July a national holiday. Under the influence of Gambetta, the ballooning Foreign Minister, a total amnesty was granted to the communards who had been exiled or deported.

For Martine Taine and Louise Michel, the long journey home from their New Caledonian prison colony was a nine-year dream come true. Their route took them right round Australia, and Martine had her fortieth birthday while the ship was docked at Sydney. She had spent the journey in a daze, with images of Denis wounded, imprisoned, dead, filling her mind.

But Sydney was the turning point. A joyful group wandered through the rocky district behind the quays and found a tavern for celebration. When sailing time arrived several days later, four of the men were missing. It was thought that they had gone off with some local companions to try their fortunes in a new continent. The master, sympathetic, perhaps envious, gave the command to weigh anchor and they were off on their voyage home, half a world away.

Louise Michel seemed impervious to all they had been through. In Melbourne she emerged unscathed from a rowdy argument between wharf labourers that had turned into a free fight; she almost missed the sailing from Singapore because she was interrogating a French merchant, a friend of her father's, on what they intended to do in Indo-China with the new rubber plants that were causing so much fuss; in Bombay the first mate had to extricate her from the police who accused her of causing trouble with the lascars unloading the ship. After that she was not allowed ashore until they had sailed past the island of the Chateau d'If, where the Count of Monte Cristo had escaped from his dungeon, and dropped anchor in the harbour at Marseilles.

For most of them, it was only the second time they had seen a French port. The weevils in the flour, the cyclone, the becalmed, sun-scorched days in the Indian Ocean, when they thought they would die of thirst, and two died from dysentery, had faded in their memories. But they had an indelible memory of leaving Marseilles nine years earlier, and the contrast was remarkable. The harbour now was alive with naval craft, from huge ironclad ships down to noisy little gunboats carrying torpedoes and launching tubes. One man excitedly pointed out a whale rising to the surface: as they got closer it turned out to be a strange steel boat. It was, one of the sailors informed them, one of the new electric submarines. 'The navy had been growing rapidly ever since the defeat of 1871,' he said. 'Was this a preparation for revenge on Germany? Was it aimed against the English? Or was it just part of the policy, so powerfully urged by Armstrong and Krupp, of being strongly armed in the pursuit of peace?'

Questions about the French rearmament were also being asked in the shipyards of Armstrong at Elswick and Krupp at Kiel. The answers were hotly disputed, but on one point there was general agreement: it must be good because it created employment.

Martine had not come on deck for the approach to Marseilles. She had relapsed into a morose state and developed a trembling that persisted even when they disembarked.

People from all over France had discovered the date of their arrival and had gathered at the quayside to meet the ship. Among them was Denis Taine. Later that evening, at the house of a local schoolteacher, a white-haired woman and a frail one-armed man went slowly up the stairs to bed, their arms entwined.

On the train to Paris, Denis brought Martine up to date. He told her how Danielle and her children had gone to London with Maurice Dupont and his mother. Maurice had a good job in publishing. He still hankered to return to Berlin, but he had lost touch with the young woman who had captivated him on his visit a decade ago. Young Pascal was working as an errand boy. Life in London seemed to be good. Even Françoise was thinking of going there. Perhaps, when they had settled down again in Paris, he and Martine might save enough to go to London.

And during those years while they were busy saving up, while Martine was slowly recovering and Louise Michel was stirring up the Parisian workers and getting herself arrested again, the nations of Europe became addicted to the deadly drug of armaments. The struggle between Armstrong, Schneider and Krupp was simply the struggle between England, France and Germany viewed through the wrong end of a telescope. Each increased his steelmaking capacity as fast as he could, believing that he would win the race.

But it was the consumers who could not keep up the pace. The railway boom started to slow down, and the steel industries were driven into selling more armaments abroad in order to survive. Business picked up as the American domestic markets were developed, but it fell off again when the United States decided to protect its own growing steel industry, leading to even more feverish efforts by the Europeans to cultivate a global market for their arms.

The irony in this latest swing was that Andrew Carnegie, the spearhead of the American steel industry, was the most peace-loving of them all and resisted seduction by the guns longer than his rivals.

When Chester Arthur became US President following the assassination of President Garfield in 1881, he ordered four modern steel warships. For four years Carnegie would have nothing to do with it. During the fifth year, his partners succeeded in convincing him that they should supply the armour for the ships. 'After all', agreed Carnegie, 'it isn't like guns; armour is purely for defence.' By the time that the United States railway boom started to run out of steam, Carnegie was persuading his partners that they should move into guns. But by 1898 his pacifism had recovered and, in an attempt to avert the Spanish-American war, he made a bid to buy the Philippines for $20 million.

Three years later, he sold his steel business and began giving away an average of $2 million a year in the cause of international peace. One of his typical creations was the Peace Palace at The Hague in Holland, the home of the International Court of Justice.

While Andrew Carnegie was flirting with the armaments industry of America, the European arms race was rushing ahead. It rode on the torrent of white hot steel that was flowing from Bessemer converters and open-hearth furnaces, now mostly lined with dolomite according to Sidney Gilchrist Thomas's basic process.

Sidney Thomas had also fulfilled his dream of becoming a rich man. In the company of Lise Schiller, he toured the continent seeking orders, modifying his process in the light of experience and above all making sure that his patents were watertight. With the benefit of his legal background, he even succeeded in extracting large sums from a reluctant Krupp. Knowing that he was consumptive, he never settled down to marry, and in 1885 he died in Paris at the age of thirty-six. Lise and his sister had been given the precise details for the disposal of his fortune; it was to be applied to projects for the benefit of the poor, as he had always planned.

When Lise returned to Germany in 1887, she found great changes in her elder brother. Kurt was now the successful and self-assured Prussian businessman. He had owed his early success to the favour of Alfred, the old Cannon King, but recently his abilities had brought him closer to Alfred's son Friedrich, alias Fritz. It was Fritz, the once chubby baby with a mighty steam hammer named after him, who had become the firm's chief diplomat. He toured the capitals of the arms-buying world being received by generals, premiers and, especially, sovereigns. On these delicate missions his confidante was Kurt.

Lise had judged well the moment of her return. Fritz Krupp was tied to the factory at Essen, taking over the reins after the death of his father. His impending visit to Leopold, King of the Belgians, was important, because Leopold, now virtually an Emperor, had personally acquired that huge region of Africa known ironically as the Congo Free State. Kurt's job was to go ahead and prepare the ground for Fritz. He would be safely occupied in Brussels while Lise was breaking the news to Dr Heinz Schiller that she had made him a grandfather, although she had not married.

The old man recovered from the shock when Lise brought in her two-year-old son to meet him. That night father and daughter sat down to work out a story to explain the tragic loss of Lise's husband. That should head off questions from those in his social circle, who were always eager to be scandalized, and avoid any disastrous repercussions on Kurt's employment with Krupp.

Kurt Schiller's visit to Brussels was a great success. He had obtained an audience with Leopold and got on famously with that enterprising monarch. He admired the way that Leopold had played off the Great Powers to obtain for himself a treasure house of ivory, copper and diamonds.

There were also rich crops, such as cocoa, and strange vines which could be harvested for their rubber, although neither of them saw much future in that beyond making solid tyres for carriages and for the Daimler-Benz vehicles that were spluttering erratically through the streets of the European capitals and frightening the horses. But they both smiled at the idea of Leopold as crusader, bringing the light of civilization into darkest Africa, protecting the natives and guaranteeing them freedom in trade.

In his hotel in Brussels, Kurt wrote to Fritz: with a colony like that to protect, here is a customer with great potential. He also wrote to his young wife, Gertraude: 'It is thrilling to find that there are still worlds to conquer and men capable of conquering them; what prospects lie ahead for our children!'

The first of their children, Baldur, arrived in 1888. He came at a dramatic turning point for the prospects not only of the Schillers but also of Germany and the world. Kaiser Wilhelm I had died in March and his successor, the humane Friedrich III, had died of cancer only three months later, leaving the state at the mercy of Wilhelm II, outstanding militarist and Krupp fancier. Kurt had accepted the convenient fiction of Lise's secret marriage in England and the tragic death of her husband in a mountain-climbing accident. He was really too busy in Essen to worry about domestic affairs in far-off Berlin.

Not infrequently Kurt was a guest at the Villa Hügel, on the occasions when some notable in the steel or arms industry came to visit his Mecca. One was a German engineer with drawings of what he called a rational heat engine. He told Fritz that he had come to Essen because it was important that the engine be built from high-quality steel. Indeed, it should, agreed Fritz, signing his name on the contract below that of the inventor, Rudolf Diesel. It would also be a handy acquisition when the time came to build panzers and U-boats.

Two visitors to the Villa Hügel were marvellously comple-
mentary. Hiram Maxim offered a licence to make his already famous
machine gun, while Alfred Nobel arrived with the smokeless gunpowder, 'ballistite', which it needed for its effective use in the field.
Maxim, a bright-eyed country boy from Maine, USA, recommended
his gun as particularly useful for 'stopping the mad rush of
savages'.

Science, or if you prefer, technology, was creeping more and more
into the military power of the advanced nations. When the British
used their Maxims to mow down the Sudanese dervishes at
Omdurman, the battle where Kitchener was in command of the
Egyptians and Winston Churchill rode with the 21st Lancers, Sir
Edwin Arnold observed that 'in most of our wars it has been the dash,
the skill, and the bravery of our officers and men that have won the
day, but in this case the battle was won by a quiet scientific gentleman living down in Kent'. The scientists, as Oppenheimer might
have said, were discovering sin. Many of them were quite liking it.

Fritz Krupp himself made a scientific contribution to the business,
following up some experiments by Michael Faraday on alloying steel
with nickel. Faraday's work in the early part of the century had
aroused little interest among the steelmakers, but suddenly the time
was ripe. Battleships now had to carry armour plating over 60
centimetres thick, and Fritz recognized that increasing the strength
of the steel, rather than its thickness, was a more sensible solution.
Henry Schneider was already making a good nickel-steel armour, but
Fritz developed a case-hardening process for nickel-steel alloys
which could be used on battleships and solved the need for gun
barrels that could withstand Nobel's picric acid explosive.

A cosy armourers club was set up, including Krupp, Vickers,
Armstrongs, Schneider, Carnegie and Bethlehem Steel (in Pennsyl-
vania, not Palestine) to control the market. It was particularly cosy
for Fritz Krupp who went on drawing royalties from England,
France, Italy, Japan, and the US for all of the armour plate produced
in the hectic race for naval supremacy, until his patents expired
in 1911. He was, of course, also making battleship armour for
Germany.

Krupp's star salesman, the man that Kurt was meant to emulate,
was Friedrich von Bulow. Already he had virtually open cheques
from the treasuries of Italy, Portugal, and Turkey in his pocket. But
privately Kurt was more impressed by the great individualist of the

arms trade, the mystery man of Europe, Sir Basil Zaharoff. Kurt admired the way in which he worked for himself rather than becoming a salaried employee of one of the great steel and arms barons. As agent for Maxim's gun factory, for instance, he drew a handsome commission on sales, and those increased enormously when Vickers acquired the firm in 1897. He also had such perquisites as $2000 a year towards the rent of his luxurious Parisian house.

He excited Schiller both by his reputation as 'The Merchant of Death' and by his grand seigneurial style. He could have been the model for Andrew Undershaft in George Bernard Shaw's *Major Barbara*, who cut through the pious suggestion that 'the more destructive war becomes, the sooner it will be abolished' by saying:

The more destructive war becomes the more fascinating we find it. No, Mr Lomax: I am obliged to you for making the usual excuse for my trade; but I am not ashamed of it. I am not one of those men who keep their morals and their business in water-tight compartments.

Undershaft also defined the true faith of the armourer in a way that seemed consistent with at least the shadowy public image of Zaharoff: 'to give arms to all men who offer an honest price for them'.

Schiller's eyes were opened when Zaharoff came up against von Bulow. The King of Spain wanted several batteries of modern guns to deal with a revolutionary situation in Cuba: who would win this highly valued order? The struggle between the titans raged on until nearly every senior Spanish officer was in the pay of Krupps or Vickers. Then came the master stroke. Zaharoff secretly donated some Krupp guns to the rebels, and King Alfonso was informed privately that his enemies were fighting him with guns from Krupps of Essen. Vickers immediately got the main contract, Schneiders picking up some flow-on orders.

Apart from Zaharoff's percentage on all Vickers's sales, he received less tangible but still useful rewards from two grateful nations. The French invested him with the Grand Cross of the Legion of Honour. The British made him a Knight of the Grand Cross of the Bath, and the University of Oxford granted him a Doctorate of Civil Laws.

But to Kurt Schiller, Zaharoff stayed largely shrouded in mystery. It was Fritz Krupp whom he increasingly came to know and to wonder at. The armaments see-saw was Fritz's particular speciality, if not invention. The technique was straightforward. An important, defensive advance, such as his nickel-steel armour, was given great publicity and sold to eager bidders to protect their battleships against gunfire. A new alloy shell was produced to pierce even this tough armour. More sales. And no sooner was a tougher armour produced than an explosive-tipped shell was invented and sold.

It was only at the close of the century that Kurt began to understand this strange man Fritz who, at forty-six, was five years his junior. He knew of his early life as the asthmatic only son of the neurotic despot Alfred, one of the richest and strangest of men who thought of his child as he thought of his new steam hammer. His mother, a strong-minded plebeian who had long given up the impossible task of living with Alfred, still managed to take care of Fritz, however, and ensured him a good marriage to the aristocratic Margarethe von Ende.

By the time that Kurt became close to Fritz and Margarethe, they had two daughters who were already old enough for their confirmation. But Fritz was starting to break away from the rigid factory existence to which his father had committed him. Recalling the happier days of his youth with his mother in Mediterranean resorts he was spending two months of each year based on Capri. Kurt was once invited for a short trip on his yacht and was delighted to see Fritz without a thought of steel or guns in his head, following his scientific pursuits by diving for, and on occasion discovering, new creatures of the sea.

But Fritz was not confining his interests to marine biology. In addition to collecting his crustaceans and fish he was also collecting handsome Italian youths. Margarethe did not accompany him on his summer vacations, and Kurt was sent back to Essen as soon as the voyage had ended. At length it emerged that Fritz went alone to a private hotel where he and his young friends disported themselves in a luxuriously appointed and perfumed grotto. Wine would flow, presents of gold brooches shaped like artillery shells would be made and caresses would be exchanged on silken couches to the sweet sounds of a trio of violins. Fireworks stood at the ready and climaxes of delight were proclaimed by volleys of rockets roaring into the sky. Added spice was provided by having a candid cameraman in attendance, to provide nostalgic souvenirs for Fritz. It was a foolhardy gesture; the cameraman was too candid and some of the copies of his pictures eventually came into the hands of the police.

The news first surfaced in Germany in the autumn of 1902 when Margarethe was sent anonymous letters containing clippings of lurid accounts of her husband's cavortings in Italian newspapers. In her distress she rushed off to the Kaiser, not realizing that in that male-dominated court she would get a most unfriendly reception. Indeed she was bundled off to an asylum in Jena.

The affair was turned into a national political battle. The social democrats launched the challenge by publishing the story in their newspaper; the conservative establishment, led by the Kaiser, wanted Fritz to keep Margarethe put away so that they could suppress the evidence and go over to the counter-attack.

Fritz carefully weighed up the proposals. He even got so far as to institute criminal proceedings against the editor but then gave up the struggle. On 21 November he went home to the Villa Hugel, played a parlour game with his daughters Bertha and Barbara, then retired to his room. In the morning it was discovered that he was dead. The circumstances of his death were obscure, but the consequences were appalling to the fatherland. Its military powerhouse, the source of its steel and of the guns, submarines and battleships it would depend upon in the coming struggle, had become the property of a sixteen-year-old girl; and until she came of age it would be managed by a woman who had just been released from a lunatic asylum.

THIRTEEN

The Day of the Dreadnought

'Sack the lot.'
Admiral of the Fleet, Lord Fisher

The twentieth century swept grandly into Europe. People began talking of a new age, an Age of Progress. Previous ages had been called after queens and kings, or after the materials on which their civilization was built: stone, bronze, or iron. Looking at mighty structures like the bridge over the Firth of Forth, the great railway networks, or the fast steel ships, it seemed for a while that the Age of Steel would be next. But science was already transforming the Industrial Revolution; with chemistry and electricity in the forefront, the new technology would become the hallmark of a society with the power to produce wealth in unprecedented abundance. Steel would soon be dethroned to become an essential but unregarded everyday commodity like air or water.

To the middle and upper classes nothing seemed able to stand in the way of their Utopian dreams. Even the toilers of industry began to taste a prosperity they had never known. Yet the seeds of discontent grew in the fertile ground of inequality. It even showed in health. Twelve-year-old boys in the wealthy English public schools were, on average, 13 centimetres taller than their working-class contemporaries. In 1917, when the British people were first given a collective medical examination, only one in three was found to be in a reasonable condition.

Indeed, the benefits of science flowed scarcely at all to people in the lower classes. They were dissipated by the leisured classes, with that playboy monarch, Edward VII, setting the pace. Flitting round Europe from casino to hunting lodge, cruising the Mediterranean in their steam yachts, the opulent Teddy-boys lived like Roman emperors while paupers slept under railway arches with only a second-hand newspaper for a blanket.

Landowners cried that they were suffering under an agricultural depression. Yet the hard-pressed Duke of Bedford still managed to provide his agent with a handsome salary, a pension, two country houses, ten servants, and three gamekeepers, together with free supplies of game, garden and dairy produce, and whisky.

Upward mobility was possible, indeed encouraged, in this self-styled free country. Thomas Lipton was one of the country's well-known grocers, but he happily raced his yachts round the Isle of Wight with Edward, the sailor-king.

These antics were viewed from across the North Sea with satisfaction. Kaiser Wilhelm was taking his sailing more seriously than these English, whom he contemptuously described as 'playing at boats'. He had read *The Influence of Sea Power upon History* by the American naval captain, A. T. Mahan. 'Control of the sea', wrote Mahan, 'is the chief element that determines the power and prosperity of nations.' A strong navy is 'a political factor of the utmost importance in international affairs'. And the nations, particularly Germany and the United States of America, had not been slow to take the hint. The pen may not always be mightier than the sword, but sometimes the two work together with deadly effect.

The United States began to build a modern navy. Following Mahan's urging, it also looked around for some overseas bases which it would need as coaling stations. An attractive starting point would be the island of Cuba in the West Indies, but Cuba was a colony of Spain. Randolph Hearst ran a virulent anti-Spanish campaign in his *New York Journal*, and it would not be long before a suitable 'incident' would precipitate the government into declaring war on Spain.

When the USS *Maine* blew up in Havana harbour on 15 February 1898, Hearst made sure that this would be the necessary incident. A banner headline read:

DESTRUCTION OF THE WAR SHIP WAS THE WORK OF AN ENEMY

and the *Journal* offered a $50 000 reward for exclusive information 'leading to the conviction of the criminals responsible'. On the front page an artist's impression showed exactly how the *Maine* must have been blown up by a Spanish mine moored underneath it. This heinous act, said Hearst, could only have been deliberate. The logic behind his assertion was breathtakingly simple: as he explained it 'not a single fact to the contrary has been proved'.

In the war that followed, the new American battleships sank most of the antiquated Spanish squadrons they encountered. The modern ships were both lighter and faster. Thanks to Krupp's nickel-steel alloys, the armour plating had been reduced to only a quarter of its earlier thickness. Instead of 60 centimetres of hardened wrought iron, the new alloy needed only 15. The United States succeeded in defeating Spanish colonialism, but it finished up by acquiring Puerto Rico, Guam and the Philippines. Mahan's theory about control of the sea was soon being put in to practice.

It was a boom time for science and technology. New materials and new powers were coming thick and fast. It became a race between those who were building a brave new world and those who were planning to knock it down. And like the Earth resting on the shoulders of Atlas, the new world was emerging on a foundation of steel.

Steel production had been rising dramatically. Over thirty years it had increased sixty-fold, from 0.5 to 30 million tonnes a year. Cheap iron and steel enabled the engineers to impress everyone with their gigantic structures. Everyone, perhaps, save for a few disgruntled aesthetes. As the 7000 tonnes of iron girders were being bolted together in 1889 to make the Eiffel Tower, Gounod and the younger Dumas were circulating protest petitions; Guy de Maupassant left the city in disgust. Yet two million visitors in its first year established it beyond doubt as the symbol of Paris. In 1940 the symbolism was turned to advantage when a squadron of British fighters flew in low over the city and dived repeatedly through its lower arches, to the chagrin of the occupying Germans and the delight of the Parisians.

While the iron tower was going up in Paris, the even greater strength of steel was being demonstrated in Scotland. The railway bridge over the Firth of Forth spread its steel wings over its two 520 metre spans, each longer than anything previously attempted, and longer even than the bridge over Sydney harbour built forty years later. William Morris, poet and aesthete, viewed the completed Forth bridge and pronounced it 'the supremest specimen of all ugliness'.

The ugliness was, no doubt, in the mind of the beholder. The fifty grey warships that Fritz Krupp had built for his friend Wilhelm II would certainly have looked beautiful to that royal patron. And just as beautiful, perhaps, to Admiral von Tirpitz, who had squeezed the money for them out of a reluctant Reichstag. His Navy Bills of 1898 and 1900 authorized the building of enough battleships to meet Britain's Home Fleet on equal terms.

Thus began the military leapfrogging that is dominating super-power politics today. For a few years earlier, Britain had passed its own Naval Defence Act, laying down that the strength of the Royal Navy must be kept at least equal to the combined naval strengths of any other two countries. And who would deny this? Least of all Krupp, who was already collecting royalties from all of the steel armour used by England, France, Japan, and the US.

Krupp, moreover, had the unquestioning support of the Kaiser in all of his activities. He certainly needed it when an enraged Admiral Tirpitz discovered that he was making a 100 per cent profit on the armour he was supplying to his own country, Germany. Even when one of the fashionable disarmament conferences drew up a proposal at the Peace Palace in The Hague, Wilhelm scrawled angrily across it, 'Who will pay Krupp's workers?' thereby propagating the cruellest confidence trick of all: the idea that armament is essential for full employment.

Meanwhile, both in Essen and in his new shipyards at Kiel, Krupp's workers had not been idle. Despite opposition from the con-servative German Navy, they had designed an all-steel boat powered by Rudolf Diesel's engines. It could travel long distances while sub-merged, a German version of Jules Verne's *Nautilus*, which became the first 'Unterseeboot' – the U1.

It was full steam ahead for steel and, above all, for the military. Nationalism, power, and profit were all on the side of the armourers; steel for railways and bridges, or for the newly arrived motor cars, did not have quite the same incentives. The greatest incentive lay with the greatest fighting machine of the time, the battleship. Guns with more powerful shells were countered by improved armour; bigger guns were met by tougher steel; and so on.

In ships of the *Majestic* class, the wrought-iron-plus-steel armour had been replaced by Harvey nickel steel plate, hardened on its outer surface by chilling to give protection against the 12 inch guns of the 1890s. By 1900 the higher muzzle velocities of battleship guns were giving the advantage to the attacker, and Harvey's plate was super-seded by an even tougher armour from Krupp.

Then Britain snatched the initiative. The arrival of the abrasive John Fisher at the Admiralty in 1903 signalled a radical reform of the

British Navy. Fisher had entered the navy as a thirteen-year-old boy serving on Nelson's flagship *Victory* at Portsmouth. He became First Sea Lord in 1904, and in 1914 he sent, secretly and against the wishes of the Cabinet, the battlecruisers which won the Battle of the Falklands. In 1915 he resigned in opposition to Churchill's enterprise in the Dardanelles.

In 1906 his campaign reached its climax with the launching of the first 'all big-gun' battleship, HMS *Dreadnought*. Although this revolutionary new ship had been designed by a committee, it was so good that it instantly made all other battleships obsolete. It had ten 12 inch guns that could blow up an enemy ship 20 kilometres away, two dozen 12 pounders to keep off the small but deadly torpedo boats, and a set of steam turbines to drive it through the water at a speed of 21 knots. Nearly 20 000 tonnes of steel went into its construction, the armour plate making a handsome contribution to the coffers of Krupp.

As Fisher's critics caustically observed, the advent of *Dreadnought* had made *all* battle fleets obsolete – including his own. The massive superiority of the Royal Navy could only be restored by taking the lead in the international battleship race that now began. And that is what the British public, urged on by their daily newspapers, soon began to demand. But while the race was in progress a strange event took place.

On a cold February day HMS *Dreadnought*, now the flagship of the Home Fleet, was riding peacefully at anchor in Weymouth harbour on the English Channel. Unexpectedly a telegram arrived from the Foreign Office announcing the imminent visit of the Emperor of Abyssinia.

The royal party was met with proper naval honours at Weymouth Station, taken by launch to HMS *Dreadnought* and given a personal tour of the great ship by the Commander-in-Chief, Vice-Admiral Sir William May. The guns, turrets, range-finders, and wireless room were all explained in detail through the medium of the top-hatted gentleman from the Foreign Office and his interpreter. The state visit came to an end with some gracious remarks from His Majesty, duly interpreted for the Admiral, and the Imperial party, magnificent in their flowing robes, departed.

The next day, headlines in the *Daily Express* and the *Daily Mirror* gleefully proclaimed:

DREADNOUGHT HOAX!

The Emperor and his retinue, it appeared, were all impostors. In particular, the young prince, Ras Mendax (Ras = Abyssinian for 'prince'; Mendax = Latin for 'lying') was a Miss Virginia Stephen, with blackened face, false moustache and beard. She was a member of the upper-class literary set, a penetrating critic of England's male-dominated society and soon to become a world-famous novelist.

Questions in Parliament were adroitly sidestepped by the First Lord of the Admiralty, even the specific point raised by Captain Faber who asked: 'Is it not a fact that certain pairs of white kid gloves were actually purchased for the occasion, and can the Right Hon. Gentleman say who will pay the expense?'

Miss Stephen's only public comment was that if the national security had been revealed as inadequate, she was glad to have done her bit for her country.

When *Dreadnought* was launched in 1906, 30 per cent of the population was living below the poverty line. The Medical Inspector of Schools in Lambeth reported the typical diet of a schoolchild: bread and tea for breakfast; bread and margarine for lunch; a penny-worth of fried fish for dinner. No fresh milk. Meat occasionally on Sundays. Some rotten fruit when they could scrounge it from below the barrows. The cost of HMS *Dreadnought* was £2 million.

HMS *Dreadnought*

FOURTEEN

Two Birthdays

24 December 1901. I walked along the Embankment this morning
at two o'clock ... Every bench from Blackfriars to Westminster
Bridge was filled with shivering people, all huddled up – men,
women and children. The Salvation Army people were out giving
away hot broth, but even this was merely a temporary palliative
against the bitter night.

R. D. Blumenfeld, quoted in *The Long
March of Everyman*, Penguin Books, 1978

Saturday, 6 December 1907, was a great occasion for Pierre Taine. To
celebrate his tenth birthday his father had promised him a real treat –
a visit to see the sights of the West End. It would help to soften the
memory of his mother's death in the influenza epidemic just a year
ago. They had left their flat in Clerkenwell soon after breakfast, the
excited Pierre clutching his new tinplate battleship (made in Japan),
which he adamantly refused to leave behind, his father, Pascal, and
his grandmother, Danielle, dressed in their best clothes. The fourth
member of the party was Roma, a little girl of Pierre's age who lived
in the flat above. Although it was warmer than usual for the time of
the year, her mother had wrapped her up well. All of them wore
muffs and scarves.

A brisk walk had brought them to the underground station where
they had gone down on a long moving staircase, deep into the bowels
of the earth. When the bright red train had come crashing out of its
tunnel and screamed to a stop beside them, Pierre had been terrified,
but with Roma there he tried hard not to show it.

They emerged into the crisp, dry air and found themselves among
the bustling crowds in an Oxford Circus gaudy with Christmas
decorations. Despite the crush of hansom cabs, horse-drawn delivery
vans and buses, they managed, after several attempts, to get across
Regent Street and set off towards Marble Arch.

Oxford Street was a continuing entertainment for them. Expensive milliners, with only one or two hats (unpriced) in the window,
brought Danielle memories of long-departed days in Paris. Pascal
was awed by the endless range of luxuries of all descriptions – dresses

costing more than a month's wages, meats, cakes and wines, delicacies from around the world, displays of the new electric lighting – a grown-up's wonderland.

The children found other things to marvel at. Pierre was the first to spot a motor car. It had stopped outside a huge shop and the driver, wearing a grey uniform with a shiny peaked cap, was carrying out big boxes wrapped in coloured paper. They watched spellbound as he strapped them on to the luggage rack, climbed in and started the engine from inside the car. Tooting his horn, he moved off down the road, steering a careful course between the horses, bicycles and buses.

Their next excitement was in watching four men standing on the pavement playing music. Pierre envied their coloured ribbons and shiny medals and pictured himself strutting about with medals of his own when he was grown up. The trumpet player had only one leg, and the man who was holding out his cap for people to put pennies in had only one arm. Further on, a man with a monkey on a string was offering boxes of matches for sale. He was wearing a pair of spectacles so dark that you couldn't even see his eyes. Then there were the newspaper sellers, shouting their cries: ' 'Orrible murder in Whitechapel!', 'Dreadnought on trial; Greatest Ship in the World!', 'Record prices on Stock Exchange!', and 'Disarmament plan offered by the Czar!'

By the time they reached Marble Arch, tiredness had overcome the excitement. Danielle rested on a bench in Hyde Park and unpacked the sandwiches while the others bought tea and lemonade from a stall. One of Roma's shoes had split, and Danielle bound a handkerchief round her foot to stop it from becoming sore.

A pale sun had emerged, and the afternoon was cool and bright. Gathered round the empty bandstand were genial ladies with strings of balloons, people selling kites, flags, and toys, and a mysterious-looking fortune teller. An appetizing aroma drifted across from the stall of a roast-chestnut vendor. Pascal bought a tuppenny kite which the children flew as they walked on through the park, but they soon brought it down when they heard the sounds of bugles and the beating of a bass drum. Running ahead they pushed through the crowd and were thrilled by the sight of a regimental band marching by, colours flying and cymbals crashing with a gusto that had them stepping out left-right-left-right until they reached Hyde Park Corner.

By now they were happy enough to stand patiently while the adults listened to the speakers performing on their soap boxes: a silvery-haired old man urging them to repent, for the end of the world was nigh; a fiery Irishman calling for 'Home Rule *Now*'; a woman (who reminded them of Danielle) proclaiming, 'Votes for Women'; an angry matron from the League of Empire Loyalists screaming for more battleships – 'We Want Eight and We Won't Wait!' echoed the poster on her platform.

Danielle was saddened. 'I've seen this all before,' she told them. 'It always leads to the same thing – war.'

'Not this time,' Pascal confidently assured her. 'France is no longer alone. The alliance of Britain, France and Russia is so strong that Germany would never dare to attack. Eight new dreadnoughts will make it even more certain, the old girl's right about that at least.'

'But isn't that just what the Germans are saying?' Danielle challenged. 'They've got their own alliance – with Austria-Hungary and Italy – and the biggest army in the world. "Peace through strength", the newspapers are calling it. More battleships to keep the balance. But the bigger the forces they get, the more violent it will be when their precious balance is lost.'

Pascal was not persuaded. 'Mum, you're still living in the nineteenth century,' he laughed, 'Come on, let's take the kids down to the exhibitions at Kensington and give them some fun.'

The rest of the afternoon was a kaleidoscope of impressions for the two children. It began with a wonderful battle between the grown-ups. Pascal announced his intention of taking Pierre to the Science Museum while the others would visit the Victoria and Albert; the attraction there was 'Dress through the Ages', with a special display of dolls and dolls' houses from all over the world. Danielle flatly refused, and when it turned out that both children were keener on seeing the models of ships, cars, and railway engines than the dolls, the argument ended.

On their way they danced round the statue of Peter Pan and paid a brief visit to the Victoria and Albert, where Pierre was fascinated by the dolls' houses and had to be almost dragged away.

Inside the Science Museum, Roma was absorbed by the model railway engines, turning handles and pressing buttons to make the wheels go round. Pierre's attention was captured by Frederick Simm's 'motor war car': this combined the virtues of the internal combustion engine with the safety of armour plate to protect the occupants from unfriendly attack. Pierre would dream of driving his Simms furiously across some far-off land, the spears, arrows and even the occasional bullets of the natives bouncing off while his trusty comrade blazed away at opportune moments with the Maxim gun. In this he was more farsighted than the War Office. They showed no interest at all in Mr Simms's vehicle, even when in 1912 it was converted effectively into a tank by the addition of tracks according to the design of the Australian engineer L. E. de Mole.

By now it was growing dark. Birthday tea was held in a café on the Strand, and the last lap was a walk along the Thames embankment to Waterloo Bridge, where the bus would take them home to Clerkenwell. Wonder of wonders, the great sailing ships were dressed overall, lanterns gleaming from bowsprit to stern and in the cabins and portholes. In the greenish light from the gas lamps on the embankment, they rode like ghostly schooners in the night. Danielle felt inspired to tell the sleepy children the story of the Flying Dutchman as they trudged along.

They were awake enough, however, to see how the benches beneath the trees and under the arches of the piers were already occupied by families bedding down for the night. Roma would not forget the sight of two children, younger than herself, struggling with the piece of torn sacking which would be their blanket.

In Sheffield, the City of Steel 300 kilometres to the north, another birthday was being celebrated. Jim Lovedale was sitting in his study dandling his two-year-old granddaughter on his knee. Times were good for Jim. Since taking over the foundry of his apprentice days he had acquired two others, and only a few months ago he had bought an engineering works, also in Sheffield. Its business in firearms gave him a perfect outlet for the special steels he was making. At weekends he played crown bowls with his old friend Harry Brearley. Harry had similar interests in steelmaking, and the friendship was both satisfying and fruitful. They would dwell for hours over a pot of beer, swapping ideas on heat treatment, compositions of alloys, or arguing on the best way of dealing with the blasted unions. Ah, sighed Jim, if only he could bring his son David to see the pleasures of the good life of a successful Sheffield steelman.

David, however, was set on a different course. That very night, even on his daughter's birthday, he'd gone off after the party to his precious Workers' Educational Association meeting. Workers' Education indeed, grumbled his father. Hobnobbing with trouble-makers like Edward Carpenter, who attacked his country for stand-ing up to the Boers. Outrageous! Look at the things he gets up to: trying to get votes for women; agitating about a bit of smoke in a healthy town like Sheffield; stirring up the workers to demand a minimum wage! He ought to be locked up. Ever since he met that American friend of his, that Walter Whitman, he's been carrying on about 'free love', if you please. Can't think where David gets it from; must be his mother's side. Perhaps it was a mistake, though, my marrying so young before I'd had time to look around a bit.

This trenchant denunciation of evil would hardly have troubled the grandfather of the baby boy lying in his ornate crib at the Villa Hügel in Essen. The baby Alfred, Bertha's firstborn, was the grand-son of the late Fritz Krupp. His father Gustav von Bohlen and Halbach had been selected by His Imperial Highness as a suitable male to head the House of Krupp. By imperial edict he would be known as Gustav von Bohlen und Krupp, a mouthful that was soon shortened to Gustav Krupp.

FIFTEEN

The Bloody International

On the one hand we have the most wonderful machinery of
production that has ever been known; on the other, the most
tremendous machinery of murder ... nothing could have been
more unexpected by the earlier prophets of democracy than the
apparent return of militarism with a vengeance at the end of a
liberal and humanitarian century.

Newcastle *Daily Chronicle*, 1900

Gustav Krupp was not just a mere caretaker of the mighty steel and
arms enterprise. It took him a year to comprehend the full extent of
his wife's empire. One of his managers, Dr Kurt Schiller, had shown
him over several Krupp factories and foundries in Essen, and
explained how he also owned large slices of minerals and industry in
Australia and India, as well as being the proprietor of the huge nickel
deposits in New Caledonia.

Gustav set himself to keeping ahead of the international com-
petition – not only Schneider, Vickers and Armstrong, but now also
Skoda in Bohemia, Mitsui in Japan, and Bethlehem and Du Pont in
the US.

One of his decisions was sufficient by itself to show that the faith
of the Kaiser in choosing him for Bertha's husband had not been
misplaced. Noting the successful use of barbed wire in the recent
Russo-Japanese war, he deduced with spine-chilling accuracy that
trenches protected by barbed wire would be needed on a large scale in
the next war. This vision inspired him to buy Germany's largest
wireworks, conveniently situated just 50 kilometres away, at Hamm
in the Ruhr.

Another decision, more secret and more related to the techniques
of steelmaking, was to build the biggest gun in the world – bigger
even than those carried on the new all-big-gun battleships. This
mighty engine of war could fire a shell to hit a target 100 kilometres
away. It needed a railway locomotive to move it around and took a
team of 200 artillerymen to operate it. As a strange sort of tribute to
his wife, Gustav named it Big Bertha. Later, even more strangely

perhaps, the captain of the plane that dropped the bomb on Hiroshima would name it *Enola Gay* after his mother.

The shells for the gun, over 40 centimetres wide, were tipped with armour-piercing steel and fitted with Krupp delayed-action fuses so that they did not explode until they had penetrated to the heart of their target. These fuses would be used throughout the war on shells going in both directions. After 1918 Krupps collected their royalties on the fuses made by Vickers that had been used in British guns to kill Germans.

Kurt Schiller was pleased with his discussions with the new proprietor. It was good to have a man at the helm again, someone you could take orders from. Over lunch he had managed to tell Gustav how he had persuaded his son Baldur not to follow his desires into the military academy but to go to the Berlin Technical Institute instead. Already Baldur was showing great promise in metallography and had mastered the recent German invention of X-rays. Now he was studying with Dr Wilm who had discovered how to make aluminium alloys which became harder as they aged. How valuable this could be for shell cases, or even for Count Zeppelin's airships, Krupp mused aloud. Kurt had also observed proudly that young Baldur was not neglecting his other duties to the fatherland. He had produced a grandson for Kurt, a lusty infant named Siegfried, who would undoubtedly become a great hero. 'Fine', nodded Krupp, 'and guess who will make his invincible sword!'

In discussing his family affairs with Krupp, Kurt had made only the vaguest reference to his sister Lise, now living in Paris with her son who was a year older than Baldur. It did not seem worth mentioning the un-Germanic name of Lise's son – Sidney Maurice Schiller – nor the fact that young Sidney was a paid organizer of the General Workers Federation. There was no point in embarrassing his host. Gustav Krupp would probably have been more than embarrassed had he known that Lise Schiller was also an organizer in Paris for the UF de F, the Union of the Women of France, and was just as active as her son in the movement for disarmament.

In December of 1907 Lise Schiller was driving her shiny Renault home through the icy streets of Paris. Lise had been visiting her friend Marie in the village of Sceaux, on the southern edge of Paris, where she had been living with her children since the death of her husband in a road accident in the previous year. Marie still worked most of the time at her laboratory in Paris, carrying on the research on radium for which she had won a Nobel prize. This week she was on holiday, and Lise had gone to see her about a petition to the disarmament conference at The Hague. A short distance ahead, she saw an elderly man about to step off the kerb. Suddenly remembering how Pierre Curie had died last year, she squeezed the bulb of the horn, emitting a bellow which must have startled the man who looked round, slipped on the ice and fell heavily to the road.

Lise was able to stop well short of him and got out from her car in time to help him to his feet. 'Are you all right?' she started to ask, then stopped as they stared at each other in amazement. 'Lise', he stammered at last, 'it can't be ...' and suddenly the two embraced, oblivious of the wind, the falling snow or even of Maurice Dupont's torn trouser legs.

As they were driving across the river to Lise's house off the rue du Faubourg St Honoré, they were pouring out reminiscences, interrupting each other, catching up on the years that had passed since they met, just before the Franco-Prussian war. Lise heard an inside story of the days of the Commune, and of the hardships of Denis Taine and Maurice's sister Martine. Denis and Martine had adopted twin girls, born in 1871 and orphaned by the massacres of Thiers's invading army. Maurice was working with a publisher and living with the others in the working-class district of l'Alésia.

Events in Europe from that Christmas in 1907 until the summer of 1914 moved rather like a Greek tragedy. But there were a few highlights. One was in Sheffield when Harry Brearley went out to the yard behind his works and saw something gleaming in the rusty pile of scrap. It turned out to be a rejected test specimen from the series of alloys he had been preparing with the aim of getting a more durable steel for James Lovedale's rifle barrels.

Fortunately he could identify the composition of this brightly shining specimen from its markings, and it turned out to be a steel containing approximately 13 per cent of chromium. He polished the specimen, intending to carry out the standard microscopical examination of its structure. When none of the conventional etching chemicals would react with it, Brearley realized that he had discovered that elusive material, stainless steel.

By 1914 the confusion in Europe was so great that it was hard to tell whether the curtain was rising on a tragedy or a comedy. But the tragedy was that even those who thought a war was coming had no idea of its duration and horror. They believed that if war did come it would be only a limited war: six months was as long as anyone would give it.

In each of the major powers people argued for keeping the peace by attaining a position of strength. Their radical opponents argued that the arms race could only end in disaster.

In May 1914 the German social democratic leader, Karl Liebknecht, told the Reichstag that 'Krupp's is the matador of the international armament industry' and spoke passionately against 'the bloody international of the merchants of death'.

The flashpoint had been reached, with the assassination of the heir to the throne of the Austro-Hungarian empire by Gavrilo Princip, an unknown Serb having no connection with the Serbian government. The stage was set for a showdown unless any one government tried hard enough to prevent it. None did.

An Austro-Hungarian ultimatum to Serbia received a conciliatory reply. Czar Nicholas favoured peace as did his cousin the Kaiser and the British Foreign Secretary, Sir Edward Grey. Andrew Carnegie, steelmaker turned pacifist, was so proud of his friend the Kaiser that he called the last chapter of his autobiography 'The Kaiser and World Peace'. As he was writing the last words, he was informed that Austria-Hungary had declared war on Serbia and the whole train of military alliances had been set alight. The shock, as his wife wrote later, broke his heart.

To put all the blame on nationalism or on the merchants of death would be an over-simplification, but that was H. G. Wells's despairing frame of mind when he wrote, in August 1914, 'At the very core of all this evil that has burst at last in world disaster lies Kruppism, this sordid, enormous trade in the instruments of death.'

One sign of the deeper reality was that war came as a relief to the governing classes in those societies. An unbearable tension had built up between the forces of conservatism and socialism. Trade unionists were proposing an agreement for a general strike to paralyse any war that might be launched. The plan was on the agenda of the International Socialist Congress to be held in October 1914.

In England the Liberal government was faced with growing problems. There were waves of violent strikes. Since the death of

Emily Davison under the hooves of the King's horse in the 1913 Derby, suffragettes had become more militant; they had already burned down over a hundred buildings. Egged on by right-wing politicians, British army officers had mutinied over Home Rule for Ireland. 'There are things stronger than parliamentary majorities,' pronounced the conservative leader, Bonar Law. On 21 July King George V called political leaders to Buckingham Palace and urged them to work out a quick solution to avert civil war in Ireland. Even quicker than an Irish solution or the International Socialist Congress, however, came the outbreak of the war.

Inflamed by the usual nationalistic cries from the politicians and the press, the initial response to the war was almost universally joyful. As the tension snapped, the English poets were carried away with a lyricism that verged on the hysterical. 'War,' wrote Julian Grenfell, 'is like a big picnic but with more purpose.' And Rupert Brooke embraced the advent of war like the arrival of spring after a dismal winter:

> Now, God be thanked Who has matched us with His hour,
> And caught our youth, and wakened us from sleeping,
> With hand made sure, clear eye, and sharpened power,
> To turn, as swimmers into cleanness leaping,
> Glad from a world grown old and cold and weary,
> Leave the sick hearts that honour could not move,
> And half-men, and their dirty songs and dreary,
> And all the little emptiness of love!

Before long the poets would be singing a different song.

SIXTEEN
Steel, Mud and Blood

Lines of grey, muttering faces, masked with fear,
They leave their trenches, going over the top,
While time ticks blank and busy on their wrists,
And hope, with furtive eyes and grappling fists,
Flounders in mud. Jesus, make it stop!

Siegfried Sassoon

The war began strangely, like a few damp squibs going off before the big fireworks show. On 22 August 1914 a patrol of the 4th Dragoon Guards encountered some German horsemen near the Belgian town of Mons. They made a successful charge and the Germans, hampered by their long lances, retreated after several of them had been killed in a sword fight. But modern military technology was about to take over. The dragoons halted their pursuit when they found themselves under rifle fire from a German battalion mounted on bicycles. It was now their turn to retire.

Later in the day a Royal Flying Corps biplane reported that massive German forces were converging on Mons. The aviators had also spotted numerous batteries of heavy artillery moving forward.

The dragoons were meeting the oncoming wave of German armies striking through Belgium at Paris. This was the master stroke, the Schlieffen plan, by which Germany expected to crush France as swiftly as in the memorable push of 1870. But already something had gone wrong. The target city of Liege had been captured, but its circle of surrounding fortresses had held on. That was the signal to bring into action Krupp's secret weapon, the Big Berthas, eight giant howitzers, each weighing 100 tonnes.

Within a week, the forts and their occupants had been reduced to a rubble of concrete, crushed bone, twisted steel and blood. But that delay had given just enough time for the British Expeditionary Force to cross the channel and link up with the French. The German High Command, far away in Luxembourg, completely lost control of the situation and, within weeks, the battle line had been drawn at the

River Marne. Both sides dug in there and feverishly extended their barbed wire and trenches until they stretched along an 800 kilometre front from the Alps to the Channel coast. The long, agonizing stalemate had begun.

The tension in Paris had risen rapidly during the first few weeks of the war as the German armies drew closer. The wounded were pouring back and filling the emergency field hospitals to bursting point. German citizens were being interned – often for their own safety – but Lise Schiller, now married to Maurice Dupont, was exempt. She would, in any case, have been exempted because of the war work she was doing, helping Marie Curie to gather X-ray equipment for use in the hospitals. With funds from the Union of Women they produced their Voiture Radiologique – a motor car with an X-ray set powered by the dynamo of the engine. This travelling X-ray station toured the shattered countryside of the Marne saving thousands of limbs and lives.

As autumn wore on the two women went further and further afield. They took equipment to military hospitals at Verdun, Amiens, and almost to the coast at Ypres, but always within the sound of the pounding of the guns.

No longer were missiles simple cannon balls or even metal shells filled with gunpowder; now they were precisely machined steel cases containing the high-explosive TNT and often several hundred lead balls according to the clever invention of Colonel Shrapnel. When exploded in the air by an equally clever Krupp fuse, the balls and fragments of the case spread over a wide area, tearing and embedding themselves in any soft materials in their way, particularly flesh.

Christmas came and went and, to everyone's surprise, the war was still going on. Lise was devoting herself to her work with redoubled energy. Maurice had died in October and Lise's son, Sidney Schiller, had enlisted immediately, leaving his wife and baby daughter, Odette, in their Paris apartment. It was, she could now see, simply his love for the old printer that had been holding him back. Maurice had never departed from his belief that the war could be stopped by international working-class action.

Sidney Schiller argued that the real enemy was militarism; Germany was the aggressor and had to be resisted. He had refrained from any direct participation until November but now was in training at an army camp near Bordeaux. Lise prayed that the war would end before he could reach the Western front.

Then, for one heavenly moment, time was suspended and a vision appeared, not of the mythical Angels of Mons, but of a future state of humankind: the war came to a stop. In sector after sector on Christmas Day 1914, field-grey, blue, and khaki figures climbed out of their trenches, tramped across the blood-soaked mud of No Man's Land and met their brothers from the other side. Gifts and rations were exchanged and treasured family photographs passed round amid laughter, singing, eating and drinking. That was the first and only time such behaviour, intolerable to authority, was allowed. If repeated it might have led to deeper exchanges of views and perhaps to an end to war. According to Frank Richards in *Old Soldiers Never Die*:

We mucked in all day with one another. They were Saxons and some of them could speak English. By the look of them their trenches were in as bad a state as our own. One of their men, speaking in English, mentioned that he had worked in Brighton for some years and that he was fed up to the neck with this damned war and would be glad when it was all over. We told him that he wasn't the only one that was fed up with it.

All ideas of a limited war disappeared in that winter of 1914. The Russians had won major battles against Austria-Hungary and driven the Germans back from Warsaw, despite losing over a quarter of a million men. The Russians were running out of munitions, and the grand duke, Nicholas, informed his allies that he could no longer mount an offensive. All was quiet on the Western front. The combatants were licking their wounds and asking themselves, for the first time, could they keep going much longer?

Germany was the most desperate. The British naval blockade had cut off many supplies, as anticipated. But most critical of all, the stock of Chilean saltpetre – the nitrate from which the explosives were made – had been almost exhausted by the unexpected ferocity and duration of the fighting. When it was gone, the German war effort would inevitably come to an end. It took a leading industrialist, Walther von Rathenau, head of the German general electric firm AEG, to bring this sobering fact to the attention of the German Minister of War. The generals and admirals were so bemused by the Schlieffen concept of a short war that they had no contingency plans going beyond 1915.

There were two escape routes: the German navy and the wizardry of German science. The Admiralty went into action by ordering the naval squadron of Admiral Graf von Spee to leave its station in the Indian Ocean immediately. Its task: to capture the key to the trade routes from Chile to Germany, the inhospitable Falkland Islands.

As von Spee sailed down the west coast of Chile, he easily defeated the small British naval force steaming up from the Falklands to meet him. The First Lord of the Admiralty, Winston Churchill, had no more idea of the significance of Chilean nitrate than his German counterparts. He formed the idea that Spee was out hunting merchant ships and might even be aiming at the Panama Canal. Just in time, it dawned on the Admiralty that the Falklands were his goal. An old battleship was sunk in the harbour of Port Stanley to serve as a gun platform. Thanks to the foresight of Admiral Fisher, a powerful British squadron had already sailed, and it reached the islands just as the German invasion was about to begin. With their 12 inch guns, the battle cruisers *Invincible* and *Inflexible* sank most of von Spee's fleet without ever coming within his range. The quest for nitrogen now had to be pursued in Germany's laboratories.

Fritz Haber had astonished the chemical world four years earlier with his nitrogen fixation process: a method of combining the nitrogen in air with the hydrogen in water to form ammonia. Now that had to be put into large-scale practice. But German science also astonished the German army when four leading scientists – Fritz Haber, Emil Fischer, Walther Nernst and Richard Willstätter – pointed out that the German chemical industry could not only synthesize scarce materials but also provide such deadly gases as chlorine and phosgene. Properly used, these might win the war by themselves. All four of these famous chemists won Nobel prizes: only Haber was nominated as a war criminal.

The military-scientific collaboration came unstuck at first when the German army tried to use a bromine-based gas against the Russians. The air temperature on the Eastern front in January 1915 was below the boiling point so that the chemical was no longer a gas; it splashed around and sank into the snow. By April, however, Fritz Haber was standing ready with his steel cylinders of chlorine near Ypres on the Western front. On 22 April he judged the wind conditions to be perfect and ordered the taps to be turned on. The effect exceeded even his expectations. His only disappointment lay in the failure of the army to go straight through the 7 kilometre gap that he opened in the enemy's ranks and seize the unprotected channel ports.

Science and war: Vickers machine gunners ready for a gas attack on the Somme, July 1916

Within a few hours after he had opened the first tap, 5000 allied soldiers lay dead on the battlefield. Another 10 000 were gasping, choking and coughing up their lungs in agony as they struggled back to waiting ambulances. One of the French soldiers, picked up by the Red Cross stretcher-bearers, who found him crawling blindly around a huge shell-hole, was Sidney Schiller.

Unfortunately for the German army, they had thrown away their element of surprise. Admitting that they had lost their chance to win the war on that April day, they despatched Haber off to try again against the Russians. His wife Clara pleaded with him not to go, but he argued that it was his patriotic duty and departed for the Eastern front. That night Clara committed suicide.

Germany had missed the chance of a lightning victory, and it faced the likelihood of being defeated by running out of explosives. Everything now hung on one man: the metallurgical engineer, Carl Bosch. In the four years since Haber's discovery, Bosch had designed and built a plant for synthesizing ammonia on a massive industrial scale, a mighty achievement that would later bring him a Nobel prize. Germany's capacity to keep fighting lay in his hands and, in May, he announced that he had succeeded. Germany could now make its own explosives without needing to import a thing.

Carl Bosch's company, the giant chemical dyestuffs manufacturer BASF, was able to return its shareholders a comfortable 25 per cent on their capital for the rest of the war. In 1916 it associated with Bayer, Hoescht and some smaller companies to form perhaps the most famous of all cartels, the German Dyestuff Industry Group, IG Farben. Its importance to the war effort appeared in September, after the carnage of the Somme, when the two chief German soldiers, Field Marshal Paul von Hindenburg and General Erich von Ludendorff, met the two leading industrialists to plan a crash programme of supplies to win the war. The two industrial leaders were Carl Duisburg, head of Bayer and spokesman for IG Farben, and Gustav Krupp.

By now the war was starting to show its true character. It was to be a hard battle for supremacy – military, political and economic – with no holds barred and science and technology increasingly important. No longer would the songs of the poets extol the beautiful youth marching on its way to immortality. After the hell of Gallipoli, the gas attacks, and the Somme, poets like Siegfried Sassoon were telling how it really was.

And through it all seeped the futility: half a million casualties at Gallipoli with nothing else to show, a million at the Somme. Wilfred Owen, killed in the week before the armistice, saw it with chilling clarity:

> Move him into the sun –
> Gently its touch awoke him once,
> At home, whispering of fields unsown . . .
>
> Think how it wakes the seeds –
> Woke, once, the clays of a cold star.
>
> . . . Was it for this the clay grew tall
> – O what made fatuous sunbeams toil
> To break earth's sleep at all?

The artillery barrages on the Western front, the latest and best products of Krupp, Vickers and Schneider, gave a new word to the English language: 'shell-shock'. Perhaps the world was becoming shell-shocked, but the huge cannon seemed after a while to have a life of their own:

We are the guns, and your masters! Saw ye our flashes
Heard ye the scream of our shells in the night, and the shuddering
    crashes?
Saw ye our work by the roadside, the shrouded things lying,
Moaning to God that He made them – the maimed and the
    dying?
Husbands or sons,
Fathers or lovers, we break them. We are the guns!

SEVENTEEN

More Steel, More Mud, More Blood

In every city of every land you can hear the passing-bell.

Yvan Goll

In the view of Sir James Lovedale the war was far from futile. Quite the opposite. His contribution to the war effort had been recognized in the 1917 honours list. For services to industry, they had said, but it was his clever use of the electric furnace to make specialized alloys that had done the trick. With it he could use the steel swarf turned out from the munitions factories, blending in nickel, vanadium and manganese to make the high-speed tool steels that the Sheffield arms factories were demanding. His three foundries had all expanded and were working round the clock. Today, he was off to London for a meeting at the War Office on a secret project of national importance.

The woman who opened the door of her Hampstead flat to Sir James that night was more than sympathetic to his troubles. As they dined and chatted over the champagne she had skilfully obtained through a friend in the Army Service Corps, she joined Sir James in denunciation of the shirkers and dissidents who were sabotaging England's war effort. Poor Sir James! Even his own son, David, manager of the new Brightside factory, a reserved occupation from which he would not be conscripted, was hobnobbing with trouble-makers.

'You know,' he told her, 'people like Edward Carpenter, and his friend the army officer, the one who wrote those weird poems and threw his Military Cross into the sea, Sassoon. You know what I'd do with them, Sylvia, I'd put them up against a wall and shoot them! In the pay of the Germans, half of them, I bet. Young David needs a damn good hiding – should have more consideration for his wife and kids. Timmy's not even a year old.'

'Never mind,' she comforted him. 'I heard today that Bertrand Russell has been fined £100 for publishing a seditious pamphlet. That should frighten them off a bit. But tell me about this new invention of yours.'

'Well, it's not exactly an invention,' he protested, 'just a small part of a big thing that's going to win the war for us. Can't say too much about it.' But, warming to his subject, and to the wine and the company, he went on to explain how his technique for mass producing hardened steel rollers had come at just the right time.

'It's impossible to break the deadlock on the Western front by pushing infantry forward against the fire of the machine guns,' he said. 'It would be like using rowing boats against a destroyer. Something more like a land battleship is needed. Tanks will be our salvation. The army just didn't know how to use them: the artillery had plastered the ground with shells for hours before the attack, churning No Man's Land into a hopeless sea of mud. In decent conditions General Fuller's new Mark IV tanks, equipped with Lovedale steel rollers, will batter their way through the enemy's lines and end the stalemate. What a wonderful year 1917 is going to be!'

General Haig's Big Push at Passchendaele was aimed at reaching the Belgian harbours: there the U-boats nestled in their pens while they were being refuelled. He made some use of tanks but only in small groups and on waterlogged ground. When his attack petered out, he had little to show for it beyond a quarter of a million casualties.

At 6.20 AM on 20 November 1917, a line of 400 tanks, one every 30 metres, advanced behind a barrage from 1000 guns, to tear a gap in the German lines at Cambrai which might have won the war outright had the General Staff shown more confidence. If armoured carriers had been provided, the troops could have poured through the gap in a breakthrough they had failed to achieve in three months fighting at Passchendaele. But the gap was closed, and the war dragged on.

Shipping losses had now reached the level of a million tonnes a month, and England would be facing starvation in 1918. But the tanks' performance at Cambrai changed everything. Cables to Essen sent the Krupp production lines rolling, although by now it was too late to save Germany. That evening the news of the victory spread across England. For a mere 10 000 dead or dying men a great breakthrough had at last been made. Services of thanksgiving were held and through that cold November night the church bells rang. Only those bells, of course, that hadn't been melted down to make cannon.

The news of Cambrai came as only a slight annoyance to Baldur Schiller: he was almost too exhausted to care. For over a year he had been totally dedicated to his huge project at the Krupp proving grounds. Since their success with Big Bertha, he and Krupp's chief ordnance technician Dr Fritz Rausenberger had been working on an equally devilish device – the Paris Cannon, which they familiarly called Long Max.

Instead of the squat appearance of the Berthas, the new gun was long, slim and elegant. The barrel was a full 36 metres in length. Its shells were only 100 kilograms, tiny compared with Bertha's, but they would reach a target well over 100 kilometres away. And the target was to be Paris. Once again guns of Krupp steel would lob Krupp explosive shells into the heart of the city. It was a technological miracle hardly to be resisted and, Baldur, working all hours and neglecting his children as much as David Lovedale was neglecting his, did not resist, which distressed his father, Dr Kurt Schiller, although for a rather personal reason.

Kurt Schiller had just retired. Despite the war he was living comfortably in his Berlin home, but his life was clouded by the inability to get any information on the whereabouts of his favourite daughter Lise. Irmgard had married well, if dully, to an aristocratic naval captain who had gained a medal but lost a leg at the Battle of Jutland. That had been the major naval encounter of the war. As soon as it was over, the Kaiser had telegraphed congratulations to Essen. The excellence of the guns, armour and shells was, he said, a triumph for the Krupp works. He did not, of course, point out that the considerable British successes in that battle also owed much to their excellent armour (Krupp) and shells (fuses by Krupp).

Nevertheless, on balance, Jutland had been a German victory. Irmgard and her husband were happy, new U-boats were coming weekly from Krupp's shipyards, and Kurt still felt confident of ultimate victory. But thoughts of Lise, last heard of in Paris just before the outbreak of war, with her French husband Maurice and her son Sidney, were heavily on his mind as he walked down the Kurfurstendamm for his morning glass of schnapps.

Lise at that moment was leaving the Hospital du Naître in very high spirits. She had been delivering a new X-ray tube to the Pasteur Institute and to her surprise and delight she met Martine Dupont-

Taine's adopted daughter Claire in the corridor. They snatched a few minutes for a beaker of coffee brewed in the laboratory.

Claire was bubbling over with the success of her work. Some time ago they had discovered that blood could be preserved in glass containers by mixing it with a solution of sodium citrate in water – a liquid very similar to lemonade. This simple technique prevented the blood from clotting. With a small addition of glucose it could be kept refrigerated or sent up to the hospitals behind the battle lines in glass bottles ready for blood transfusions. A transfusion no longer had to be a clumsy arm-to-arm affair.

A few years earlier Karl Landsteiner had shown how to classify human blood into four main groups. Blood of one type could be safely transfused into a person with blood of the same group, but certain mixings could cause serious illness or even death. With this knowledge and their new citrate technique, they had already saved thousands of lives that would otherwise have been lost.

What relief both women felt at this example of the beneficial use of science to set against such monstrous abuses as shells and gas. Claire was planning a reserve supply which would have refrigerated stocks of the different blood groups always available to be drawn – a 'blood bank' as she called it.

When Claire found herself working with a blood bank it was in 1918, although not at the front as she had expected. Over the last year tremendous changes had transformed the face of a war in which all combatants were reaching the breaking point. Russia had withdrawn, turning after its revolution to its severe internal problems and thereby releasing a million Germans for the Western front. The British blockade had brought the German people close to starvation, but Krupp's U-boats were exacting a fearful toll of the Allied shipping. Once again they had started attacking merchantmen. In 1915 they had abandoned that practice after the loss of American passengers when the *Lusitania* having been sunk had threatened to bring America into the war.

Now the Germans had accepted the likelihood of American intervention. They were gambling everything on a major campaign at sea to prevent the American troops from crossing the Atlantic in time to stop their final thrust which would conquer France. And that final thrust had, indirectly, brought Claire back from the forward hospitals to Paris.

Thousands had died, bleeding to death in the muddy swamps that the shells had churned out of the fertile fields and woods in the valley of the Somme. Claire's job had been to organize blood supplies for the French hospitals serving the southern sector of that front. But two days after General Ludendorff launched his last offensive at the end of March 1918, another front suddenly appeared: the heart of Paris.

Long Max, Krupp's gigantic gun, had been assembled in a wood behind the German lines. It looked like something out of Jules Verne. Mounted on a platform carried on two separate railway tracks, it pointed directly towards the French capital 120 kilometres away. It was the supreme high-technology terror weapon of its day. Gustav Krupp had received a Doctorate of Philosophy from the University of Bonn for Big Bertha but, surprisingly, after the 1918 gun, they did not make him President of the Academy. Long Max had been developed from a 15 inch naval gun, and it took an admiral and a crew of sixty seamen to fire it. Their preliminary calculations had to take into account the temperature, pressure, humidity, and curvature of the earth's surface, and the admiral presided over an instrument panel as complex as on a Jumbo jet. On the command 'Feuer!' a shell zoomed into the sky, reaching a height of over 30 kilometres. Three minutes after firing, it exploded somewhere in the middle of Paris. The very first shot, on 23 March, landed among the pedestrians crossing the Place de la Republique.

Although the barrel wall was a 40 centimetre thickness of steel, the bore was expanded slightly by the force of each firing. The shells were therefore all different and carried an identifying number so that successive shots fired slightly larger shells. It was necessary to pre-heat them in an oven to ensure the correct size.

Going home from the hospital where she had been training nurses for the new blood transfusion unit, Claire found a rope holding back an agitated crowd at the entrance to the street where she lived. Through the dust and the rubble everywhere she could just make out the crumbled shapes of two of the tenement buildings. Was her grandmother safe? And her sister and the children?

She ran desperately through the neighbouring street until she reached the house. Two teenage children were standing in the doorway looking out anxiously at the damage. 'Thank heavens you're safe,' gasped Claire, 'but where are your mother and grandmother?' Their mother was upstairs, it appeared, sitting with Martine who had gone to bed after the shock of the explosion. Although physically unhurt, the old lady seemed in a sort of trance, as if her mind was far away. Perhaps she was going through the streets of New Caledonia in her prison garb under the hot South Pacific sun. Or was she re-living the scene nearly fifty years ago where, as a young woman bursting with life, she had stood in a street and looked incredulously at the carnage wreaked by a shell from one of the Krupp cannon outside the city? Whatever it was, with a strange smile on her face Martine lay in her bed and died peacefully three days later.

The bombardment ceased abruptly on 9 August. On the previous morning 300 British tanks, supported by aircraft, had come out of the mist to smash through the German lines over a 20 kilometre front near Amiens. A small-scale attack by General Monash's Australian Corps had already shown that the barbed wire, the mud, and machine gun defences were powerless to stop them. Ludendorff called 8 August 'the black day of the German army'. The steel monsters would sweep inexorably forward until 11 November, the day when the war to end war came to a stop.

So great had been the effect of the tanks that, as General Haig wrote in his final despatch, 'When real tanks were not available in sufficient numbers, valuable results have been obtained by the use of dummy tanks painted on frames of wood and canvas.'

Two leading British military thinkers were already looking ahead to the wars of the future. General J. F. C. Fuller, 'the brains of the Tank Corps', and Captain Basil Liddell Hart, gassed on the Somme in 1916, drew up blueprints for tank warfare. Without much honour in their own country, their ideas had a powerful effect on foreign armies, particularly in Germany in the 1930s and in Israel after World War II.

Even then, in 1918, two German soldiers were also taking careful note of the power of the steel-armoured vehicles: Kapitan Heinz Guderian, inventor of the Blitzkrieg, and an obscure Austrian corporal in the 16th Bavarian Reserve Infantry, who had been wounded and gassed on the Western front and had won himself an Iron Cross. That young hero was Corporal Adolf Hitler.

EIGHTEEN

A World Fit for Heroes

The news sent me out walking alone along the dyke above the
marshes of Rhuddlan, cursing and sobbing and thinking of the
dead.

Robert Graves, *Goodbye to All That*, 1929

As the echoes of the last shot died away at 11 AM on 11 November,
there was a surge of joy and hope throughout Europe that lasted
about as long as the victory celebrations.

Disillusionment had gone deep. As Lenin said, the Russian armies
had already voted with their feet. Now they were defending their
homeland against armies from all over the world. That very morning
5000 American troops were attacking Archangel on the Baltic coast.
Winston Churchill sent British units to join French, Polish and
Japanese forces engaged in an attempt to smash the young republic.
In Germany, Field Marshal Hindenburg had advised the Kaiser that
he could no longer count on the loyalty of the army, and massive
desertions were taking place. Over the following weeks, as the shock
of the armistice wore off, rioting began even in the victorious
armies.

The New Year brought widespread mutinies involving about
100 000 soldiers in the British army. But that consummate politician
Lloyd George had already seized his opportunity. Amid the cheering
and the ringing of bells he called the 'Khaki election' and swept into
power before Christmas with a huge majority for his Liberal-
Conservative coalition. It was a boom time for electioneering
slogans, and the fiery little Welshman knew just the nerve to touch.
For the returning soldiers, sailors and airmen it was 'Homes fit for
heroes to live in'. 'Blimey, yus', was the Cockney's response, 'it'd take
a bleedin' 'ero to live in 'em.'

Three years later the *Daily News* carried a report of an ex-
artilleryman living in London with his wife and children in a shanty

of tarpaulins and tin. 'If they'd told me in France that I should come back to this,' he said, 'I wouldn't have believed it. Sometimes I wished to God the Germans had knocked me out.'

The shooting war had, it seemed, reverted to a social war, fought with less obvious weapons. Gustav Krupp had his back to the wall, defending his steel empire against the avenging Allies who wanted to take it over. The first few years were the hardest. He got over the shock of finding himself on the list of 900 German war criminals and became confident that he would never be brought to trial. His confidence was justified.

How did Krupp come to be listed as a war criminal? In the flood of recrimination, it became fashionable to lay the blame for the war at the door of the arms manufacturers. Never again would they be allowed to get away with it. Ramsay MacDonald, soon to become the British Prime Minister, described his horror at seeing the Turkish guns on the Dardanelles with their brass labels 'bearing the name of a British armaments firm'.

The 1935-36 Royal Commission records Lloyd George's feeling at the Peace Treaty meeting:

[that] Krupps had had a very pernicious influence upon the war spirit in Germany, and had stirred it up a good deal for their own ends . . . There was not one there who did not agree that if you wanted to preserve peace in the world you must eliminate the idea of profit of great and powerful interests in the manufacture of armaments.

Clemenceau had similar things to say about Schneiders; Woodrow Wilson had no time for any of them. As President of the United States, he inspired the statement of six objections to arms manufacturers which was incorporated in the Covenant of his beloved League of Nations.

But harder for Krupp to accept was the Allied Control Commission's insistence on his dismantling half of his famous steelworks. They were also set on destroying all of the guns, warships and arms-making plant that had been the mainstay of the German military machine. He made sure, of course, that all of the oldest equipment was included in the half that was removed, but the blow was softened a little by the bizarre action of the British officer in charge of the destruction of guns. Krupps denied that there were anywhere near as many guns as appeared on the colonel's list. 'Well then, you'll have to make some more then, won't you?' was the reply.

Once again the Krupp production line went into action until the full number of guns was made up and duly despatched to the Control Commission to be smashed up.

Krupp's really serious problems lay in his workforce. He was now saddled with 100 000 employees and virtually no orders. The workers and soldiers setting up democratic ruling councils all over Germany posed a greater threat than the Control Commission. His decision was immediate. Of the Kruppianer 70 000 were paid off and given a railway ticket home, to Poland more often than not. The hard core, 30 000, were reassured of their safe position in the Krupp organization, providing that they toed the line.

Baldur Schiller, dedicated as ever, was busily turning his wartime experience to maximum advantage. Krupp's only hope of survival was to produce heavy steel goods for the peaceful years ahead – no longer guns and tanks but bridges and trains. The engine that had trundled Long Max along the Laon sector to bombard Paris was hastily redesigned as the standard locomotive of the Prussian State Railways.

Visiting Berlin in 1919 to settle the railway contract, Baldur had stayed for two nights with his sister Irmgard and her husband. Walking across the park together, Irmgard and Baldur witnessed a strange event. A speaker standing on a pair of steps was haranguing a gathering of workers. Already they appeared to be sufficiently incensed to be on the point of marching off to capture the Town Hall. As Baldur was turning back to get Irmgard away from possible danger, one of the supporters reached up and tugged the speaker's sleeve, insistently drawing his attention to the notice: 'It is Forbidden to Walk on the Grass'. At once the improvised platform was moved to the pathway. As the crowd re-formed it was clear that the emotional tension had been lost. Baldur laughed and reminded Irmgard of a saying of de Tocqueville's: 'There will never be a revolution in Germany: the police would not permit it.'

Irmgard's husband, the veteran of Jutland, found it no laughing matter. He said this socialistic government was letting the country go to the dogs. A firm hand was needed. If they couldn't see that, there were plenty of battle-hardened men who would do it for them. The men who'd kidnapped and shot those traitors, Karl Liebknecht and Rosa Luxemburg, had shown the way.

At the time Baldur felt that this was excessive. The Kapitan was understandably embittered by the loss of his leg, the decline in his fortune, and the defeat of his country. The threat by the Bolsheviks to his comfortable social system admittedly did not help. But as time went on Baldur began to think that there was something in his attitude. Riots and strikes proliferated. A Soviet government set up in Bavaria was overthrown only with great difficulty. The Deutsch-mark started on an ominous slide downwards. Were they now to lose everything?

For the next few nightmarish months it was touch and go. An armed right-wing coup was only defeated by a nationwide general strike that brought the country to a halt. The workers of the Ruhr had risen and 70 000 members of the Red Soldiers League, fighting pitched battles with the police, succeeded in capturing the entire Krupp works.

The Ruhr was officially demilitarized but, without protest from the Allies, the German army moved in, recaptured Essen, Dusseldorf and other towns where workers' republics had been declared, and massacred many of their prisoners. The moderate Weimar republic, by courtesy of the army, had gained a reprieve.

After the initial postwar surge of liberation, the balance of power was swinging strongly to the right, though as yet the civil authorities were restraining the most extravagant excesses. A coup starting from a beer cellar in Munich was overthrown after some bloodshed. Siegfried Wagner was sitting in his hotel window watching a Nazi procession marching down the street with Field Marshal Ludendorff at its head. Suddenly machine gun fire rang out. Police moved in among the sprawling bodies and found, among the wounded, the wartime air ace, Hermann Göring. They also discovered and arrested the little soldier from the 16th Bavarian Reserve Infantry, Corporal Adolf Hitler, who had dislocated his shoulder in the crush. Hitler received a lenient sentence; it put him in the Landsberg prison just long enough to write the blueprint for German fascism, *Mein Kampf*.

In another prison cell, far to the north, sat Gustav Krupp. He was serving a seven-month spell for inciting a riot when the French were occupying the Ruhr. Both men were widely held to have suffered unjustly, and both soon acquired the status of national heroes.

Instead of writing his own *Mein Kampf*, Krupp contented himself with running the business from his luxuriously appointed cell. He was probably safer inside. Outside there were strikes and riots and, more threatening to the middle classes, inflation raged beyond control. At the outbreak of war it took about four marks to buy a dollar. By January 1923 it took 20 000 marks, and by June 100 000. The rate soared to five million in August, fifty million in September and 50 000 million in October. Wives met husbands at the factory gates and rushed to the shops with their wages before another slice was lopped off their value.

The end of the road came in November when the rate hit four million million to the dollar. To buy a newspaper could cost you a barrowload of million mark notes.

To a clever businessman there are no bad times. Although the middle classes and pensioners saw their savings wiped out, and many were literally starving, farmers and property owners were smiling as they paid off their mortgages with mere pocket money. And Gustav Krupp as usual was ahead of the pack. He had even been permitted to issue his own money – Kruppmarks. This was a harder currency than the official marks, and he used it to pay off debts and acquire suitable companies that had gone bankrupt.

Happiest of all were the visiting tourists: they could live like emperors and empresses for a few dollars, francs or pounds. In 1924 the French withdrew from the Ruhr and the economic wizard, Dr Hjalmar Schacht, brought the longed-for stability by wiping the slate clean and starting with a brand new currency, the Reichsmark. It was easy to remember the conversion rate from the old money: one Reichsmark was equal to one million million of the old marks.

When the war ended, Marie Curie wrote to her friend Albert Einstein in Berlin. Albert, she had been told, had tried unsuccessfully to establish a league of European nations: only his prestige had protected him from the wrath that descends upon pacifists in wartime.

She was relieved to hear that he was safe and greatly amused by his stories about the attempts being made to test his theory of relativity. On the day the war broke out, a party of German astronomers was busily setting up equipment in the Crimea to study the eclipse on 21 August. During the few moments when the light of the sun was blacked out, they were going to measure whether starlight was bent as it passed near the sun. Einstein had predicted that there would be a very slight bending, approximately 0.00014 degrees. The expedition was financed by Gustav Krupp.

Inflation! German postage stamp, 2 million marks overprinted on 200 mark stamp

As Einstein explained, however, his first calculation had been wrong. The angle of 0.00014 degrees was what Isaac Newton could have calculated assuming that the sun's gravity would attract the little particles of light ever so slightly as they whizzed by. Einstein's new theory included the strange concept that space is 'curved' by the presence of matter. This led him to predict just *twice* as much bending as before. Fortunately for him, the outbreak of war had prevented the Crimean expedition from making its measurements, and he had discovered his error in time.

It had now become a crucial test of Einstein versus Newton. British expeditions were setting out to view the 1919 eclipse and their results, weather permitting, should settle the matter. Whatever the answer, Einstein remarked, the theory was very beautiful: if the astronomers turned up with the wrong result, he would have to feel sorry for the Creator. But there was no need. Both expeditions gave results in agreement with Einstein and not with Newton. It was, perhaps, the highest point of his scientific career.

One sunny afternoon in 1926 five members of a League of Nations committee on Intellectual Co-operation were sitting at a table overlooking Lake Geneva and drinking tea. Between Einstein and Marie Curie sat an Indian doctor and a civil engineer from Canada. The young Englishwoman at the end of the table, freshly graduated in history from Cambridge, was Joan Lovedale. Fascinating though it was, listening to these two famous scientists chatting, she felt that there were more important matters that they should be talking about. She'd had to endure a blazing row with her grandfather in Sheffield, the steel baron Sir James, before she could even get here, and she wasn't going to waste any time.

'I know that gravity and radium are important,' she started off, 'but don't you think the numbers of people affected are really very small? They aren't popular subjects, and they don't have much to do with peace or war, outside of science fiction. I think we should stick to things that people are concerned about, that give them strength from sharing their experiences instead of fighting each other. Take the steelworkers in my grandfather's foundries. They're hostile not only to him but also to the workers in your Krupps and your Schneiders as well. And with their jobs at stake, who can blame them? How to tackle the unemployment problem internationally, that's the sort of thing I think we should be talking about.'

Marie Curie's gaze softened as she met the younger woman's rush of enthusiasm. 'You know,' she said, 'you're really talking about politics. That's fine in its place, but we can only make any progress here by keeping right away from controversy. The kind of things we can deal with are health services, or how to share out the bands of the wireless waves.' She went on, 'How about "the weather" for a popular subject?' smiling at Joan's startled look. 'It's not just that it's popular, it can be vital to the future of the world. Look at the tragedy in Russia. The wheatlands of the Ukraine were ravaged by my own country, Poland, and now, before they've had a chance to recover, they're hit by drought. Tens of thousands are starving. The more we learn about the weather, and how to predict it, even if we can't control it, the more efficient will be the production of food. This committee that you're so critical of has already planned an international bureau of meteorology. Isn't that a start?'

Before Joan could reply Einstein had given an encouraging chuckle and observed that, with scientific weather forecasts, at least the steelworkers would know when it was safe to go out for a picnic. Her passion for social justice pleased him, and he was sure that Joan was right about the importance of reaching out to as many people as possible. It was the way to bring a stop to war. The people must say so themselves, he believed, and direct action might be necessary, by refusing to bear arms, for instance.

He was starting on his favourite themes of disarmament and world government when the bell rang for the next session. As they strolled in, Joan could hear Marie Curie talking about the coming marriage of her daughter Irene to the atomic physicist Frederic Joliot, but her main attention was directed to questioning Einstein about life in Berlin, for that was where she was going to stay on her way home from Geneva.

Since the murder of his friend von Rathenau, possibly by agents of the police, life had become rather uncertain, particularly if you happened to be a Jew or a communist. The big industrialists – people like Thyssen and Krupp, the steel barons, or the new chemical giant IG Farben – were stronger than ever. The rumours were that they were starting to re-arm Germany in defiance of the Versailles treaty. As for social life, she would see for herself. All Einstein would say was that it was – interesting. Pre-war morality was no more, and Berlin now outdid Paris as a centre of art, music, drama, science, and a night life of an almost unbelievable variety. Yes, he smiled, she would see for herself.

Joan did not reach Berlin. A telegram from her father urged her to get back as soon as the conference was over. Thanks to the weakness of the trade union leaders, the general strike had been broken. The government had been ruthless; Sir James had cut the wages of his steelworkers; David had taken their side, and there could be real trouble.

Sitting in the corner of her railway carriage, with the flat country-side of Flanders rolling by, Joan frowned at the English magazine she'd picked up at the station bookstall. 'Bevin Concedes Victory to the Government,' it announced. This Ernest Bevin who had given in tamely to the threats of Baldwin and Churchill was the same Bevin who had proclaimed that he would never surrender, not even if the shedding of blood became necessary. Now there would be cuts in wages, an increase in hours of work, victimizations. The meagre unemployment benefits would be slashed, and the unions would be crippled. No wonder David had been alarmed. No wonder there was trouble at the steelworks.

By the time she reached Sheffield it was too late. In a final scene Sir James had banished David from the works and from his life. His younger son had been installed as manager even though he was just a quiet accountant who had nothing of the old steelman's feeling for the Sheffield crafts.

David Lovedale and his wife had taken their ten-year-old son, Tim, to live in Southbourne, down on the south coast. Buying a boarding house near the sea, they set about making a new life. For a few years they led a dreamlike existence in that haven for retired colonels and their ladies until, in 1930, the waves from the Wall Street crash of October 1929 awoke them to harsh reality.

Riding high, despite the depression, Baldur Schiller looked back on the 1920s with satisfaction. The old firm had survived riots, occupation by the French, strikes and lock-outs that had spread throughout the Ruhr valley and brought many lesser firms to ruin. Krupp stainless steel Endura KA-2 had been chosen as the finest steel in the world to crown the top of the Chrysler building in Manhattan.

Krupp's reputation had also been enhanced by the invention of a new material for making superlative cutting tools. It was like a super-hard steel, but it wasn't really a steel because there was no iron in it at all. It was made by mixing tungsten carbide powder with cobalt, pressing the material into a block and then heating it in hydrogen. A piece of the finished material, brazed to a steel shank, made a tool that would cut steel at such high speeds that it became red hot but still went on cutting. Baldur had even seen glass machined with one of these tools as a demonstration.

Use of this Widia, as Krupps called it, greatly speeded up production of the peaceful products which were all they were allowed to make. But, as a secret memo from Gustav Krupp recorded, they also cut to one twentieth the time required for producing a grenade.

Despite the Allied Control Commission and the terms of the International Steel Manufacturers' cartel that had just been set up, Baldur was well aware that the design of equipment for the next war was rapidly going ahead. Blueprints of tanks, guns, and submarines were carefully drawn up and filed secretly away, even though they could not yet be produced.

And Baldur was not the only one who was aware of this. A popular story in Europe described the plight of a German worker in a factory ostensibly making children's tricycles. In the months before

Christmas he had succeeded in smuggling home one part after another until he had acquired a complete set. On Christmas Eve he had been assembling the pieces in the back room for several hours when his wife called out asking how much longer he was going to be. 'I don't know,' he replied. 'Every time I think I've got it together it turns out to be a machine gun.' It seemed that everyone knew what was going on; everyone except for the governments of Britain and France, but perhaps they just didn't want to know.

> . . . and they shall beat their swords into ploughshares, and their
> spears into pruninghooks; nation shall not lift up a sword against
> nation, neither shall they learn war any more.
>
> Isaiah, 2:4

After the time of Sidney Gilchrist Thomas, the steel industry became
the barometer of the world's fortunes. Checked briefly by the
1914–18 war, it soon resumed its upward swing. In 1930 it suddenly
swung round to STORMY. World steel production plummeted. The
depression had struck.

Businessmen were jumping from the windows of the steel-framed
New York skyscrapers while the world wondered what was going
wrong. Following the Biblical injunction, the steel swords had been
beaten into steel tractors. Great ocean liners, such as the *Bremen* or the
Mauretania now ploughing the Atlantic, were consuming 50 000
tonnes of steel apiece. Just one of the great bridges spanning rivers
and harbours could take a quarter of a million tonnes. Less spectacu-
larly, though more pervasively, the white-hot rivers of metal were
flowing from furnaces, forges and rolling mills into cars, railways,
airships, bicycles, houses and factories all over the world. Yet half of
the plants stood idle and silent, like the workmen at the street corners
in each of the great industrial cities.

Was this to be the price of peace?

Was rearming the only way back to prosperity?

And would that lead to yet another agonizing war?

TWENTY

Smoke Gets in your Eyes

They asked me how I knew
My true love was true;
I of course replied
Something here inside
Cannot be denied.

   Popular song of the 1930s

Not until February 1933 did Gustav Krupp make up his mind to throw in his lot with the Nazis. Of course, his eldest son Alfried had been in the élite corps of the SS for a couple of years now, but Gustav regarded that as much a part of growing up as the fast cars, the women, and the wild parties at Riviera resorts. Many of his best people, including Schiller, were members of the Nazi party. A true son of old Karl was Schiller, with his two fine sons marching around with swastika armbands.

Most of the heavy Ruhr industrialists were backing Hitler financially, and Krupp's rival steel baron, Fritz Thyssen, was in the forefront. But Krupp had so far been very circumspect. He had spread his contributions evenhandedly across the whole range of the anti-communist parties.

Even though the Nazis were the most popular and the most likely to hold the communists in check – they were beating them up in the streets almost daily – he was worried that their national socialism might be a form of socialism after all. And whatever else, he was not going to stand by and see Krupps socialized. Those brown-shirted thugs, the SA, were the real menace. Their leader, Ernst Röhm, was talking wildly about nationalization and taxing the profits of industry to help the workers. But on 20 February Krupp met Hitler, and inside an hour he had made up his mind.

The setting was in Berlin, at the house of President of the Reichstag, Hermann Göring. The audience: two dozen hand-picked leading industrialists. The speaker: Adolf Hitler, democratically elected Chancellor of the Reich, although only in a minority government, and staking all on a victory at the elections a fortnight ahead. The speech: a masterpiece.

Hitler, putting aside the pose of ranting demagogue, revealed himself as a powerful and persuasive thinker. He could see the viewpoint of the captains of industry as clearly as they could. And he made no bones about stating that he needed them as much as they needed him. It was evident that the Nazis offered the only sure bulwark against communism. As for the future, he asked, how could he hope to rebuild a strong and flourishing German state without the full support of the nation's powerhouse, the great industries producing its coal and electricity, its iron and steel, its chemicals and the huge range of technical products for which it was unsurpassed?

He needed their support to carry on the struggle. But he could only seek it if he could guarantee industry the security and stability it required: stability of the currency; a disciplined labour force; freedom from trade union disruption. They must not become the victims of spiteful taxes aimed at the destruction of the very capitalist system that had made Germany great. Such taxes were promised by the communists: they had even been proposed by radical elements inside his own organization. His audience was aware that he was speaking of the brown-shirted stormtroopers, the Sturmabteilung or SA. He gave them a personal guarantee that he would not countenance such punitive measures: they would threaten the entire programme to which he had dedicated his life.

Krupp was greatly moved. As the senior industrialist present, he made a short speech of appreciation, and when Göring called for contributions he started off the tangible support by tossing in a pledge for a million Reichsmarks.

The next day, as the Nazi campaign swung into action, the magic name of Krupp became a key part of the massive assault by newspaper and radio. One week later, the Reichstag burned down. According to plan, Göring accused the communists: in the notorious Berlin trial, Göring's fraud was exposed and he was reduced to stammering incoherence by the Bulgarian, Georgi Dimitrov, but the damage was done. In the elections on 23 March, Hitler romped home. With the aid of the centre parties, he achieved the two-thirds majority he needed to pass the law creating a totalitarian state. The Nazis could now make their own laws, without any reference to parliament.

The way was clear for them to build up heavy industry and to re-arm Germany for its imperial mission, just as Hitler had set out in *Mein Kampf*. Only one danger remained – opposition from frustrated middle-class members inside the party. They were still insisting that the socialism in national socialism still sounded threatening. They had revelled in the destruction of the trade unions, the removal of the right to strike, and the forcible suppression of the left-wing parties. Now they wanted the other half of the bargain: political control of the army and constraint on big business.

The Nazi leaders came from the war generation and shared in the national phobia about being stabbed in the back. They determined on ruthless action. Their moment came a year later, in the summer of 1934, and it started with a wedding in Essen.

Ostensibly Hitler arrived in Essen on 28 June to attend the wedding of the local gauleiter. A more likely reason was to meet privately with Gustav Krupp. Earlier in the month, Ernst Röhm had sent four of his leading SA officers to force their way into Krupp's factory and address the steelworkers on the coming 'second revolution'. Three million brown-shirted stormtroopers stood in readiness under Röhm's command. Between the army and the SA hung Hitler's life. A council of war between Germany's leading politician and its leading military industrialist was imperative.

After the wedding, the visit to the steelworks and the private meeting with Krupp, Hitler and his cavalcade of black Mercedes Benzes headed south for the village of Bad Wiesse near Munich. In the dawn they arrived at the hotel where the storm troop commanders were sleeping, summoned there by the führer. They entered quietly. At a signal the bedroom doors were burst open by SS men with drawn revolvers. Hitler himself awakened his close friend Röhm and his blond young aide Count Spreti. They and the other SA leaders were arrested and shot.

In July, Hitler came to the Reichstag to account for the events on that 'Night of the Long Knives'. He explained how they had discovered a plot by Röhm and his henchmen to take over the state. His audience, at first silent and apprehensive, warmed to his tale and finally rose cheering to his climactic declamation: 'In that hour I was responsible for the destiny of the German nation, and for twenty-four hours I was the supreme court of the Reich myself.'

A thousand revolutionary stormtroopers died that night, and the threats to the army and to big business had gone. Hitler was safely in the saddle. With such loyal allies as Krupp, the Cannon King, he would lead Germany to greatness.

The first account of Hitler's bloody purge reached Southbourne at six o'clock. Tim Lovedale was in the den at the top of the house talking to a friend when they heard the passionless voice of the BBC announcer coming from the wireless set. Tim was down from Cambridge for the summer vacation, and John Austin had cycled over from Southampton to stay with him. That was quite an effort for the studious John. With his stooping figure, his tanned skin and dark, curly hair, he made a striking contrast to his blond, willowy friend.

Tim's athletic build and his way of moving denied his affected pose of fashionable indolence. His romanticism had taken him into the arts, but he felt frustrated by his tutor's refusal to recognize either the importance of or the romance in science. No visitor to the den could mistake his feelings. Pictures of steamships, trains, and aeroplanes adorned the walls, with pride of place to the green King Arthur class engines of the Southern Railway – *Sir Galahad, Excalibur*, and *The Lady of the Lake*. Scale model Bentley and Mercedes racing cars were in various stages of completion. A finished model of the liner, *Mauretania* stood on a bookcase where Keats and Shelley jumbled with Macaulay, Burke and *The Modern Boy's Book of Scientific Wonders*.

Twirling slowly on a thread from the ceiling was John's favourite, a blue and silver seaplane. This was the Supermarine seaplane that had won the coveted Schneider trophy and taken out the world air speed record at 407.5 MPH. His house in Southampton overlooked its hangar, and he had often watched the sleek machine being pushed out on to the river before taking off for its trials.

The plane's designer, R. J. Mitchell, was so pleased with its performance that he developed it into an elegant bird-like monoplane for the RAF, which he called the Spitfire. The designers of its engine, Rolls-Royce, were equally pleased and went on to develop the engine they called the Merlin. Six years later the Spitfire-Merlin combination, with several thousand young pilots, would stand between Hitler and the conquest of Britain. The British government, which had turned its back on Spain and resisted all efforts at collective security, hardly deserved such luck.

John had a good source of inside information about aircraft development. His father was an engineer in the steel and arms giant, Vickers-Armstrong, which had just taken over the little Supermarine company. Vickers had learned the takeover game during the years of the depression. Like Krupps, it had no orders for its favourite product, armaments, and in its struggle for survival it had swallowed up the Elswick works where Armstrong had started long ago.

The latest hobby was wireless. A home-made, three-valve receiver occupied the centre of Tim's table, displacing tennis racquets, magazines, tools and bits of Meccano. The news it had brought them from Germany launched them into one of their habitual arguments over war and peace. When Japan had invaded Manchuria, it was John who had made Tim see the tragedy of the League of Nations' failure to act. Tim's friends at school hardly noticed the event; it was much too far away to get any publicity. Even South Wales or the Tyneside – where one man in three was unemployed – were too far away for them to know what was happening inside their own country.

John was aware of all of these things: sometimes, Tim thought, too aware. Instead of playing tennis, going to a dance, or even just sitting and listening to a swing band in a night spot, he preferred to brood over the ills of the world. Perhaps it was the influence of his Jewish mother. Refugees from Germany were staying at his home, and recently he had become more serious and preoccupied than before. He was very shaken by the news.

'Let's go for a walk along the cliffs,' he suggested. 'I really need to think about this Hitler affair.' Sitting among the pines, looking over the sea towards the coast of Brittany, they mulled over the events of that unsettling year since they had left school, John for his technical studies, Tim for history. 'Could you still be a conscientious objector,' demanded John, 'now you've seen how far Hitler will go to get what he wants? What will your precious Cambridge anti-war group have to say now?'

Tim was unimpressed. 'I don't think this is going to change them. After all, what's the panic if one gang of cut-throats devours another? If there is a threat to peace, it comes from the Merchants of Death. You told me yourself how your dad's firm is only making its huge profits because of the arms business.'

John seized on the point triumphantly. 'Not just getting back; they are back! They're paying out a whacking dividend – their first for years – and the shareholders are jumping for joy. So, for that matter, are the factory workers. All thanks to the arms trade. They think the Japanese invasion was a blessing because China and Japan are both now buying British weapons.'

Tim started to object, but John raised his voice. 'Did you know what condition the government made when it bailed out Armstrongs?' he asked fiercely. 'That they should go in with Vickers and concentrate on their traditional business – meaning, of course, guns and tanks and warships?'

Tim spoke scornfully about a government that could spend £100 million on guns and battleships when they were reducing the benefit to an unemployed worker and his family, but he was cut off by John. 'Would you rather they finished up as slaves in Hitler's brave new world?' he challenged. You might as well join Victor's clique and be done with it.'

Victor was the son of the local gentleman's outfitter, a pale, fastidious youth who spent most of his time at home in his private museum among his collection of fossils, butterflies, birds' eggs, and postage stamps. His latest joy was a working model of one of the new traffic lights: he would sit with great satisfaction watching it change colours. But recently he had been spending less of his time at home, ever since he had formed a local branch of the British Union of Fascists.

Tim was of the opinion that Victor's group would never reach double figures, and he accepted the suggestion with laughter. 'Don't kid yourself that the guns are going to be used against Hitler, John. They want them now to help their exports. The long-term aim is to frighten the French and Germans and turn them towards the East. As long as Hitler faces Austria, Poland and Russia, they'll be happy.'

The coloured lights along the promenade had twinkled into life in the gathering twilight, and holidaymakers were gaily thronging round the piers, queuing up for the pierrots and the concert parties. As John and Tim watched, a rocket soared into the sky and burst into a hundred spangles to the oohs and aahs of the admiring crowds. South Wales, hungry shipbuilders marching down from the North, all of that was a world away. And who cared about the gang battles of a few Germans you'd never even heard of?

The strains of a dance band floated faintly up on the summer breeze, its lyrics apparently intoned by a herniated tenor:

    . . . so I smile and say,
    when a lovely flame dies
    smoke gets in your eyes.

TWENTY-ONE
The Deadly Rehearsal

Hard is the stubborn steel:
Warm blood soon
from thee shall flow!

Siegfried, Act I

It seemed innocent enough, the soft wind whispering through Bayreuth on that summer night in Germany. Three times Siegfried's trumpet call rang from the balcony of the strange building created by Richard Wagner for his music drama *The Ring of the Nibelungs*. Three times the wind had wafted it over the restaurants in the surrounding gardens, summoning the last of the opera-lovers to return. In the afternoon they'd watched the fearless hero Siegfried forging his steel sword 'Nothung'. In the second act they watched him using it to kill the dragon Fafner. Accidentally tasting its blood, he became able to understand the song of the birds in the forest. One was singing of a beautiful maiden asleep on a mountain crag and guarded by a ring of fire. Just as it was leading him towards this wild spot, the curtain had come down for the long dinner interval.

In the glittering crowd were three impeccably dressed gentlemen engaged in earnest conversation. Overhearing the words *blood*, *steel* and *gold*, in an odd mixture of Spanish and German, a casual observer would have thought that they were opera enthusiasts. Certainly they were taking it very seriously – their hotel register showed that they had come all the way from Spanish Morocco. For fifty years people had made the annual pilgrimage to Bayreuth from places further away than North Africa, and the audience at this July 1936 festival was no exception.

A more interesting conversation was going on in a theatre box between Adolf Hitler, Hermann Göring, and some high officials from the Nazi party's foreign department. The führer has been speaking rapidly but softly, telling them that the dominant factor in the Spanish situation was the iron ore. That would be vital for Germany in its preparations for war. Now he relaxes and returns with a smile to their earlier question: how realistic was the dragon that they had seen expiring in a cloud of smoke and flame?

'Very convincing', he replies, 'but it didn't have a chance against Siegfried. I'm sure that his sword was made by Krupps of Essen.' Their laughter dies down as the theatre lights go out, and in complete darkness the prelude to Act III begins.

Siegfried is climbing the mountain, guided by a fiery glow from a distant height. Suddenly the bird flies off in fright, and he finds his path blocked by a tall, one-eyed man wearing a large hat and carrying a spear. The audience has met this character before: they know he is really Wotan, the chief of the gods, the representative of the old order. Hitler leans forward eagerly as Siegried becomes impatient with the old man's warnings and smashes the outstretched spear with a stroke of his sword. There is a flash of lightning, a clap of thunder, and Wotan vanishes for ever.

Siegfried fights his way through the flames to the top of the rock and finds the sleeping Brunhilde, still in the armour of a Valkyrie goddess. He wakens her with the traditional fairytale kiss, and slowly she rises, her glorious soprano thrilling the theatre. After an extended exchange of pleasantries, their mounting passion amply reflected in the music, they clasp each other rapturously as the curtain falls.

Leaving the theatre between the ranks of his SS guards Hitler, like most of the audience, feels that he is walking on air. He is trembling with the memory of the cadences and crescendos as his Mercedes sweeps him away down the avenue to Wahnfried, Wagner's old house where Hitler stays while he is attending the festival.

Meanwhile the three impeccable gentlemen from Morocco have struck up a conversation with the senior SS officers in the foyer. One introduces himself as an officer in the nationalist Spanish air force. The others are Nazi businessmen living in Morocco. They have not, it appears, come to Bayreuth just for the pleasure of watching Siegfried. They are urgent emissaries from General Franco, who last week launched a revolt against the republican government of Spain and is now seeking military aid from his friends. They are promptly whisked off to their assignation with Hitler at the Villa Wahnfried.

In the lounge, surrounded by fading sepia photographs of great opera singers and with Wagner's piano in the corner, Hitler is parading up and down in a joyful mood. The elation of Siegfried is still with him as he wields an imaginary sword against an imaginary dragon. 'There', he declaims, 'that is the dragon Bolshevism: see how I finish it off.'

An hour later, after a penetrating cross-examination of the visitors, he agrees to help the Spanish rebels. Junkers aeroplanes will be sent at once so that the general can ferry his troops across the water to the mainland of Spain. War material, including tanks and Krupp 88 millimetre guns, the steel sinews of a rebellion, will follow by ship. Göring has walked over from Franz Liszt's old house across the road, and he speaks enthusiastically in support of the plan. Although the foreign ministry will object, it will be an important step in preventing the spread of communism through Europe. 'And,' he adds thoughtfully, 'it will be the first real test for my Luftwaffe.'

In a flood of champagne toasts and operatic arias played on one of the new electric gramophones, *Unternehmen Feuerzauber* – 'Operation Magic Fire' – is launched. The sword of steel has been forged and the blood of half a million people will soon be flowing into the soil of Spain.

It is strange that no one thinks of putting on a record of the sequel to Siegfried: *The Twilight of the Gods*. It is just as beautiful, although it ends with the hero dead and the palace of the gods going up in flames.

Four months later it was a sharper wind that was whistling through the Spanish fishing village of Port Bou. A grubby little train, newly arrived from Perpignan, was steaming fussily at the station, proud of itself after chugging along the Mediterranean coast, burrowing under the edge of the Pyrenees and emerging triumphantly at the coast in Catalonia.

Some of the passengers had already emerged: peasants with flat sandals held tightly by the blue ribbons wound round their legs, and fishermen in rope-soled espadrilles. Staying aboard were a few Spanish militiamen, one with a bandaged head, and a cosmopolitan group of twenty or thirty people whose only common feature seemed to be a minimum of luggage. Had it been summer their bulging knapsacks would have suggested a hiking club on holiday. At the French customs they had put on an excessive show of boisterousness, all declaring themselves as tourists, and since breakfast at Perpignan they had been singing rousing songs of a dubious character.

Enrico, the tough metalworker from Milan, and Odette, the young French doctor, were arguing heatedly whether to change trains here or at Barcelona. The peacemaker was a soft-haired English youth, Tim Lovedale, looking more like a poet who had lost his way than one of the robust hikers of the 1930s. He persuaded them that they must all stay on until Barcelona. There they would change for Valencia and a local train would take them to the training camp at Albacete.

Tim's friend John had so far been out of this multilingual argument. Now that the matter was settled, he climbed down to the platform, and they all followed suit, loading up with fruit, bread, cheese, and cigarettes. A droning from the sky briefly halted their activity. In 1936 a flight of aeroplanes was still an unusual sight. Enrico identified the sound as a squadron of Savoia bombers flying westwards low over the sea. A training flight from Sardinia? Or, perhaps, support from Mussolini for the nationalists in the south?

A bugle blast by the station guard cut short these speculations, and they piled back on board, refreshed though sobered by their glimpse of the realities of war. A rotund Bavarian started up a song, and their spirits rose as the little train gathered speed on its way to Barcelona.

In contrast to Tim, who had clearly become more light-hearted than ever after meeting Odette, John was grimly serious. He managed quite a long conversation with the militiamen, questioning them about the weapons in use at the front. They seemed impressed by his knowledge of grenades and machine guns. His experience in the Officers' Training Corps at his college, which he also took seriously, was useful. The next stage of his training was completed before the train reached its destination.

Christmas in brilliant sunshine among the orange groves of Albacete was almost unreal for them. Madrid had been bombed repeatedly from August to November, at that time an act of unbelievable barbarism. Heinkels and Junkers of the German Condor Legion had carried out the operation, gaining the battle experience they wanted and making a mockery of Franco's promise: 'I shall never bombard Madrid – there are innocent people living there whom I have no wish to expose to danger.'

Arthur Koestler, in Spain as a war correspondent for the *News Chronicle*, did not pretend to be objective. 'If those who have at their command printing machines and printer's ink . . . remain neutral and objective in the face of such bestiality,' he wrote, 'then Europe is lost.' And, in that case, 'it would be time for Western civilization to say good night'.

The motley crew of anarchists, Christians, liberals and atheists that Tim and John had for Christmas company were certainly not prepared to say good night. They had paused from their intensive training sessions for some unrestrained feasting and merrymaking that many of them felt might be their last. Madrid was now directly under attack by the fascists. Columns of Mercedes tanks supported by Fiat aeroplanes were being fought off by the republicans with the few Russian planes and armoured vehicles they had been able to get.

John sat drinking with some of the camp instructors, determined not to miss a chance of getting some useful knowledge. Tim, still rankling a bit at his failure to get transferred to the French ambulance unit where Odette was working, joined in some singing on the verandah for a while, then drifted over to listen to the camp wireless set. His rudimentary Spanish was improving rapidly. He had coped with the rousing proclamations of the popular government speakers, like the call by the communications minister Fernando Valera:

Here in Madrid is the universal frontier that separates liberty and slavery. It is here in Madrid that two incompatible civilizations undertake their great struggle: love against hate, peace against war, the fraternity of Christ against the tyranny of the church . . . This is Madrid. It is fighting for Spain, for humanity, for justice, and, with the mantle of its blood, it shelters all human beings! Madrid! Madrid!

But he could not manage (or stomach) the psychopathic ravings of General Queipo de Llano, which they sometimes heard coming from the powerful German transmitter in Seville. This gallant officer, commander of Franco's second division, fancied himself at the microphone and gave daily performances of his art. It was a unique experience to hear a serving general, in the middle of a campaign, broadcasting hour-long diatribes of propaganda and threat. John needed reassurance that the translation was accurate when he heard:

Our brave Legionaries and Regulares have shown the red cowards what it means to be a man. And incidentally the wives of the reds too. These communist and anarchist women, after all, have made themselves fair game by their doctrine of free love. And now they have at least made the acquaintance of real men, and not of milksops of militiamen. Kicking their legs about and struggling won't save them.

Any doubts John may have had that they were pulling his leg vanished a few weeks later when a war correspondent from the British paper, the *News Chronicle*, visited the camp on his way to Málaga. He was introduced to the trainees as Arthur Koestler, a man who knew his way around and who had interviewed Queipo de Llano in Seville. The general had answered his first questions frankly, boasting that they were going to turn Spain into a state modelled on Nazi Germany. Then he launched abruptly into vivid descriptions of the atrocities committed by the republican armies. 'By the end of his invective, he was breathless,' said Koestler; 'his eyes flickered from side to side and spittle oozed from the corners of his mouth.' Now he was commanding the army advancing on Málaga. Koestler departed for the scene of the action, wishing the trainees good luck when they reached Madrid.

Unfortunately their luck did not last quite so far. On 6 February, 30 kilometres from the capital, an attack had been launched. The republicans were desperately holding on to their positions between a mountain range and the Valencia road. The British brigade, their training still unfinished, were rushed to help, arriving on the night of 11 February. John and Tim shared a blanket through that freezing night, waking at dawn with a shake from their company commander, a London bus driver.

The rolling gunfire from the distant hills gave Tim a tightening feeling in his stomach. Those were the dreaded 88 millimetre guns, known to the brigade as Krupp's crackers. They were deadly accurate. Pressed into service as anti-aircraft guns, they had succeeded in bringing down several of the Russian aeroplanes that the brigade relied on for air cover. It was rumoured that their shells were tipped with armour-piercing steel for use against the few republican tanks.

The sun climbed higher, lighting the western slopes of the hill and picking out the tips of the olive grove, where they had made their base, and the little rills, where they had dug in their few machine guns. Tim was sharing a rifle with another raw and nervous youth. Between times he had to act as ammunition carrier for the machine gunners. One of them was John, who had turned out to be an expert with the machine gun and had even given a reluctant Tim a few lessons on how to work it.

While Tim was wrestling with his problem as a pacifist who had got himself involved in a real battle, he felt his mouth go dry. John had pointed out some movement on the hill in front of them, confidently assuring him that it was the Moors taking up their positions for the battle.

The sounds of gunfire drew closer. The order came to load and be ready. A rattle of a machine gun on their left was answered by rifle fire from the hill, and a roaring behind them as two Russian tanks plunged over the ditches like rowing boats pushing out to sea over the breakers. Almost at once a salvo of shells plastered the grove, making their whizz-bang sound that would soon become familiar – to those who survived.

As the second tank lumbered past the clump of bushes where John lay tensed behind his gun, it was pierced by a hit from a shell. Tim watched aghast as it lurched across the grove, coming to rest in the ditch with its engine still clattering. To his astonishment, Tim found himself wrenching open the trapdoor on the turret, quite unaware of covering the ground across the grove. Climbing inside he came face to face with the reality of war: a piece of the armour punched out by the shell had ricocheted round and round the inside of that steel box shredding the crewmen inside it like a meat mincer. The compartment was painted in blood.

By late afternoon the Moors were pressing the grove on both flanks, and the firing had intensified. Tim was now the sole possessor of the rifle. The other rifleman had died when a grenade had been lobbed at them from an adventurous Moor who had worked his way almost up to the ditch. Catching a sudden movement, Tim swung the rifle round and fired. Half deafened by the shot, he saw a figure jerk up and topple, with what seemed agonizing slowness, backwards into a heap. Tears stung his eyes. He was choking back the bitter fluid in his throat when it dawned on him that John had stopped firing.

His instant reaction was a credit to his instructors at Albacete. He flung himself flat on the ground and squirmed his way behind the line of bushes. John lay there beside his gun, trying to stem the blood that was swelling through a gash in his tunic. At that moment the order was given to retreat. Grabbing the machine gun, Tim sprayed a couple of bursts in the general direction of the attackers, then turned his attention to binding up John's wound. Confident now that he could manage the gun, he persuaded John to work his way back to the waiting ambulance. John could hear the gun firing behind him for a time during his painful progress but, as he reached the clearing, it fell silent.

The command to retreat had reached the drivers, and already their engines were ticking over. One by one the vehicles bumped their way slowly over the forest path until they met the road and sped off round the bend.

High on the side of Pingarrón, General Heinz Guderian had been observing the action. Now that it was over, he lowered his Zeiss binoculars and cursed roundly. Those stupid Russians. They were as stupid as his own General Staff. By using the tanks as casual support for infantry, they were simply throwing them away. This would be used as more evidence against him. When he got half a chance with his Panzer divisions he would show them how to use tanks. Fast mobile columns, with close air cover, striking through the enemy like a bolt of lightning. As he had described it to the führer, it would be a 'blitzkrieg'.

Emerging from his thoughts he realized that the firing had died away and that the valley before him was bathed in the pink glow of sunset. The long shadows seemed unnaturally dark and mysterious, the tree tops sparkling. As his gaze passed across a small wood on the far side of the valley, an orange light flashed out for a few moments, flickered, and then disappeared. Guderian rushed into action. 'Enemy vehicles moving out of that wood,' he snapped to his aide. 'It may be their tank harbour. Get on to the commander of the 88 battery immediately.'

The hush of the evening had descended gratefully on the weary survivors. They sat, still and silent, awaiting the order to move off now that the wounded had all been taken away by ambulance or truck. A shrill whistling followed by a series of explosions burst their world apart, shattering both the beautiful trees round the clearing and the little group of people nestling inside it.

Arganda's village hall was completely blacked out when the convoy drew up outside it. The villagers had taken great pride in patching up the shutters and curtains so that not a peep of light could reach the attention of those bombers that prowled the sky so menacingly every night. Funny how loud they sounded after dark. Just as if there were a thousand of them up there.

John was barely conscious of being carried into the hall and laid on a camp bed. Weakened by shock and loss of blood, he thought he was having a nightmare when shadowy figures took hold of his aching shoulder, pierced it with sharp needles, and fixed a tube to his arm leading to a large apparatus on a trolley beside the bed. By the morning he had recovered sufficiently to realize what was going on. He even managed a weak smile for the nurse who brought him tea, and a warmer smile of surprise and relief when the doctor arrived and was Odette Schiller, one of his companions on the train. How long ago that seemed now.

Odette's professional calm was broken by the loss of Tim, but later that day she found time to return and talk to John. She was proud of the little hospital that the French medical unit had created, and particularly of their mobile blood bank. They were putting into action the brilliant innovations of Dr Trueta and the Canadian doctor, Norman Bethune. Casualties, for example, were treated as near to the front as possible. This meant that blood transfusions could be given within a few hours – sometimes even minutes – instead of after the often fatal delays in getting back to a main hospital in Madrid.

This radically new approach would be a more significant event in military history than the flights of the Messerschmitt 109 fighters now getting their first taste of blood in the skies over Madrid. In particular, it saved the life of John Austin, and uplifted the spirits of the exhausted Odette.

The defence of the valley bought vital breathing space for the defenders of Madrid. After the youthful American contingent had served its turn, the whole area was captured by the rebels. The survivors of this Lincoln Brigade, who in later life would often suffer for their participation, were wont to recall their time there by singing choruses to the tune of the Red River Valley:

> There's a valley in Spain called Jarama,
> It's a place that we all know so well
> For it's there that we wasted our manhood,
> And the rest of our old age as well.

Heinz Guderian had seen all he needed. He had a harder battle to fight. The Chief of the General Staff was deeply hostile to the formation of separate tank units, which was Guderian's plan for the Panzer divisions. Tanks should be kept in their place, supporting the infantry, he'd growled. Heinz Guderian had two urgent visits to make. First he must get the support of Krupp, the steel king. With that backing he could talk directly to the führer.

Heinz Guderian arrived in Essen when Gustav Krupp was riding high. The star performer in Spain was undoubtedly his 88 millimetre gun, the Flak 36, the development of which had been the work of his son, Alfried. Gustav had rewarded him, as a thirtieth birthday present, by making him director of War Material and Construction.

Guderian discussed strategy with Gustav Krupp, but the real work came in a long session with Alfried and one of his technical managers, Baldur Schiller. After listening to the general's vision of the speed and effectiveness of the mobile armoured divisions, Baldur went home and wrote to his son Siegfried. He urged him to transfer at once into the Panzer Corps: they would soon be the élite of the Wehrmacht.

Guderian was now in a strong position for his meeting with the führer. Hitler asked him precise questions about the lessons of Spain and received precise answers. One: the tank had apparently been a failure as a decisive weapon. Two: the Russian, French and British high commands had fortunately drawn this conclusion, although it was erroneous. Stalin had even cut tank production down and was allocating his existing tanks to infantry divisions. Three: German aircraft had initially been inferior to the Russians, but the new Messerschmitt fighter and the Heinkel bomber were both superb war-winning machines. Four: the bombing of Guernica and Madrid had provided exactly the concrete evidence needed for his theory of lightning war. It should start with dive bombing of key cities to disrupt communications and cause civilian panic. This would be synchronized with fast-moving armoured divisions, which would pierce the enemy's positions and drive far behind his lines. To the Channel ports he added, by way of a vivid example.

Hitler needed no further encouragement. The performance of the Krupp 88s had already persuaded him to advance the date of the war. Guderian's theory fitted in perfectly with his plan. The French would be cut to pieces before the British could get there. But that problem might not even arise. He had information that the British would not attack. Their aim was to hold on to their enormous empire and wait for him to turn eastwards towards the Soviet Union.

The interview terminated abruptly when a message came that the cars were waiting to take Hitler on his summer pilgrimage to the opera festival at Bayreuth. Winifred Wagner had prepared his

Russian tanks going into battle against the rebel fascist army,
Spain, 1936

reception and a stunning new production of *The Ring* was to be
given.

Hitler danced his characteristic jig of delight as he prepared to leave
the Chancellery. He'd heard a lot of exciting things about this
production. He particularly wanted to see how they dealt with the
forging of the magic sword, and with the Tarnhelm, the helmet that
made its wearer invisible and thus able to strike without any warning.
There was nothing he liked better than a secret weapon.

TWENTY-TWO

Krupp's Last War

Remember your humanity and forget the rest.

Einstein-Russell Manifesto, 1955

At dawn on 1 September 1939, two little boys in the border village of Rezyn were lying in bed whispering to each other. It was important not to wake their parents: getting them up in a bad mood could spoil their holiday at its start. Today they were going to Warsaw to stay with their aunt. It should be a sunny autumn day.

The elder boy went to the window to see if there were any clouds. 'Come and see this,' he called, pointing excitedly to the silvery-white stripes running across the sky from beyond the western hills. The boys opened the window wide and heard a deep throbbing in the distance. At the tip of each stripe they could just make out something like a pale blue bird. Some of these blue birds were weaving in and out of the lines, tying knots in the white trails as they went.

As they were puzzling over this strange sight, a group of cavalry-men came riding past their house, galloping up the hill through the village with a shiny gun carriage in tow. Gunfire sounded from over the hill and turned into a roaring and a rattling as three large tanks came lumbering down towards them. Close on their tracks was a squadron of motorcycles followed by an armoured car. The boys gasped when they recognized the swastika flag flying by its wireless mast. An officer, young and tall, wearing an enormous black hat with a long feather in it, was standing beside the driver looking back to the hill where more tanks were appearing.

As the car went past them the young officer looked up and saw the white faces of the two nightshirted figures at the window. He doffed his velvet hat and waved it at them with a huge grin. They laughed with relief and waved back. Only after that reassuring smile from

Captain Siegfried Schiller did they become aware how frightened they had been.

But now, to spoil their fun, their parents came bursting into their bedroom. Despite their loud protests their father grabbed the boys and hastily pulled them away from the window. Their holiday was off, he grimly informed them. There would be no room for them on the road to Warsaw that day.

So began World War II: tanks against horses, just as World War I had begun with machine guns and bicycles. John Austin and his friends knew better. The war had really started three years before, in the groves and valleys of Spain. There was a young Manchurian soldier who might have claimed, had he stayed alive, that it began four years before that. But he, like Tim Lovedale, an unknown, unrecorded pacifist, had died in a vain attempt to prevent it. John Austin's warnings had fallen on deaf, often wilfully deaf, ears.

Now there could be no arguing. Exactly as John had predicted at the Munich sell-out, when Czechoslovakia was carved into pieces for Germany, Poland and Hungary, here were the steel horses of the Nazis galloping eastwards. And what sleek and powerful beasts they were, these Panzer Kruppwerke IVs, the latest armoured triumphs of the Krupp works! Gunther Grass, in *The Tin Drum*, called them 'stallions from the studs of the Krupps von Bohlen und Halbach, no nobler steeds in all the world'. And what could stop them before they reached Moscow? Would they keep going until they reached Vladivostok, where they could link up with their Japanese friends to make a steel band stretching across two continents from the Atlantic ocean to the Pacific? Was *Mein Kampf* about to come true?

The answer came a fortnight later when the Soviet army advanced half-way across Poland, bringing a temporary halt to the onrush of the Nazi armies. Hitler's next move, to the dismay of Victor Adams and his fascist friends in England, would be towards the west. It was only a year since Foreign Minister von Ribbentrop had visited them and convinced them that German ambitions lay solely in their drive to the east.

The entry of the Wehrmacht into Paris on 14 June 1940 warmed the hearts of Germans everywhere. Major Siegfried Schiller, sporting his new iron cross, came away exultant from the briefing in General Guderian's headquarters. The general was understandably piqued by Hitler's refusal to let him carry on to take Dunkirk and cut off the British retreat. Surely the way he'd taken Sedan had shown that he could be trusted to finish the job in Normandy? An attack with 1000 planes followed up immediately with his fast-moving 19th Panzer Corps? But no doubt the führer had good reasons for holding back. Some argued that he was doing a crafty deal with his friends in England. Schiller didn't really believe that, but it was clear that his father's judgement had been wise: the best place for a young German was with the Panzers.

Pity about his young brother Manfred, though. Because of his obsession with flying he'd become a Luftwaffe pilot. But they'd taken him out of the Luftwaffe for special air ministry duties, dealing with the aircraft factories. Perhaps they'd picked on him because of his father's position in Krupps.

In the big house on the hill at Essen, Alfried Krupp was equally elated. The arrival of the iron ore from the captured Norwegian mines had whetted his appetite, and it could glut itself on ores from Lorraine, a steelworks here and a gun factory there, as the bounds of the Reich spread ever wider. The map on his wall had coloured pins earmarking booty from Leningrad to the Ukraine. Such prizes softened the harsh realities of war. For Alfried Krupp these had started when his brother Claus lost control of his plane while testing an oxygen mask for high-altitude flying: he crashed to his death in the Hurtgen Forest. Soon afterwards, his cousin Kurt, interned as an enemy alien in England, was drowned when the merchant ship transporting him to Canada was sunk. Alfried managed to exclude from his mind the uncomfortable fact that the ship had been sunk by a Krupp torpedo fired from a Krupp submarine.

One way of excluding unpleasant facts from his mind was to concentrate on the pressing problem of how to meet the almost insatiable demands of his factories for labour. In similar straits the British had actually taken large numbers of women into their factories. For the true German woman that, of course, was unthinkable, but now that the Reich included millions of non-Germans, as well as the Jews, the possibilities were immense . . .

On that summer's day in Paris, Dr Odette Schiller was far from elated. Trucks were disgorging load upon load of steel-helmeted Germans to set up their camps in the parks, armed guards patrolled the streets, tanks stood at crossroads, the main buildings had been taken over, the buses had stopped, chaos was everywhere. None of that had surprised her. Her depression came from the sight of so many flags and swastikas, so many of her neighbours ready to welcome the invaders or, at the least, to go about their business as if nothing unusual were happening. She even felt glad that her father wasn't here to see it. His poor old lungs had kept him going for twenty years since the Somme, but last winter had been too hard: a chill had turned into pneumonia and ended his wheezing existence.

It suddenly came to Odette that many of her forward-looking friends had already been organizing themselves into a resistance movement, and the thought cheered her up. Perhaps she, too, might find some useful way to resist.

Alfried Krupp had a whole year to think about his problems. Hitler's taste for astrology encouraged him to choose 22 June 1941, the anniversary of the French surrender, to launch his steel juggernaut eastwards against his most hated foe, the Soviet Union. 'Bolshevism', wrote Goebbels in his diary, 'will collapse like a house of cards.' With maybe a touch of wishful thinking, the British press announced: 'The German armour will go through Russia like a knife through butter.' Winston Churchill, mighty in his misjudgements as in his judgements, proclaimed that the Finnish campaign had exposed the military incapacity of the Red Army. His experts at the War Office agreed. They said that the Russians could hold out for six weeks at the most.

The irrepressible Siegfried Schiller was happy to be in action again. Speeding his tank squadron through the dense Russian pine forests, he seemed to be confirming the British forebodings. A month's hard driving had brought them via Minsk and Smolensk to within 300 kilometres of Moscow. Guderian now had his eyes fixed on the capital that had defeated Napoleon. But Hitler said No. Like Krupp in Essen, he had his coloured pins stuck in the granaries, mines and steelworks of the Ukraine. Under protest the Panzers detoured to join von Rundstedt's armies at Kiev, but although they captured a million prisoners to send home to the labour-hungry Reich it was not until early December that Siegfried halted his squadron in a wood on the outskirts of Moscow.

While Guderian was halted before Moscow, Japanese bombers were swooping through a misty morning to shatter some of the mightiest warships in the world that were riding peacefully at anchor in Pearl Harbor. Three days later and half an ocean away, some of their colleagues sent the British warships, *Repulse* and *Prince of Wales*, to the bottom. *Repulse* was an old battlecruiser but *Prince of Wales* was a brand-new battleship equipped with the latest anti-aircraft guns, radar, and armoured decking. The day of the dreadnoughts was over. Never again would anyone design another battleship.

Six months earlier the *Prince of Wales* had started the attack that sunk the Krupp-equipped battleship, *Bismarck*, three days after it had disposed of the British battlecruiser, *Hood*. A million tonnes of the finest steel were destroyed, with only misery to show for it and no awareness of what might have been built instead.

For many years the loss of a ship or a gun had given Krupp the opportunity to build an improved model – or, preferably, two. But in that drive to the east the Krupp machines were facing a threat quite new in their history: the tanks that came from the woods to hammer them completely outclassed the Krupp monsters. 'Up to this time', wrote Guderian, 'we had enjoyed tank superiority, but from now on the situation was reversed.' A year of attack and counter-attack along the front culminated in the German debacle at Stalingrad in January 1943, ending the myth of German invincibility. It was the turning point of the war.

In Essen, seven Krupp executives, calling themselves The Small Circle, were meeting in a basement to revise their plan for the assassination of Hitler. Three attempts had already ended in failure, owing to last-minute changes in his schedule. Unaware of the plotting going on in the next building, Manfred Schiller sat in the deep air raid shelter of the main works. Looking oddly immaculate in his Luftwaffe officer uniform, he was re-reading a letter by the dim light of the shelter:

Dear Manfred

I'm sending this with a friend who leaves tonight for headquarters in Berlin. My writing is shaky because I'm using my left hand! I'm lucky to have even that because we were caught overnight in the open and frost has taken three fingers from my right. We're still stuck here, but not through any fault of our division. During the winter our general was dismissed for trying to pull us back from this hopeless position. Since then we've been steadily picked off by patrols and now we're being crippled by the frightful cold. There's little hope of holding on much longer.

The bearer who will bring you this is trustworthy, so I tell you these things now, as I may not be able to write again. All of our dreams seem to have gone wrong. This morning I watched the robins twittering on the snowy branches, impatient for the spring, and for the first time I suddenly felt like an unwanted guest. The whole tragedy that we've brought to this unhappy land hit me. Then we got the news from the south: they tried to march a million prisoners – civilians and soldiers – back to work in the Reich, but nearly all of them died on the way. It's too appalling, Manfred, I've given up trying to understand the conduct of this war . . .

Swallowing hard, Manfred stuffed the letter back in his pocket because the sirens were starting to sound the all clear, and they had to leave the shelter. It had been handed to him by Colonel von Stauffenberg of the General Staff. The colonel had been gentle in breaking the news to him of his brother's death, yet Manfred felt that it was more than just kindness of heart: somehow he was being tested, weighed up, for a reason that he couldn't at that moment guess.

Outside the shelter distant searchlights were still frantically sweeping the sky. They'd scored one success already that night, but they were hungering for more. One of a squadron of Lancaster bombers on their familiar journey down the Ruhr valley had been suddenly picked out like a theatrical star in the spotlight. Weaving and twisting like a falling leaf, it had met its fiery end from the guns of a more agile nightfighter.

It was too late for Manfred to go home. Home was only about 20 kilometres away, in the little village of Liebheim on the banks of the river Möhne, but it would be impossible to get past the roadblocks when a raid was on. He tried to telephone Marie to let her and the children know that he was safe, but the lines were closed. He felt relieved. Marie would have made some disparaging remarks about the Krupps, and you couldn't be sure who might be listening. Ever since the half-starved slaves had started arriving in Essen – Jews from the concentration camps, Poles and Russians – she had been getting more upset, and when the recent deliveries had been seen to be gaunt, terrified young women, and children, not more than ten years old, forced to do hard labouring all day in the open yards, she'd flown into a rage. It was all he could do to restrain her from writing to the führer. That would be madness, even though he'd heard from a friend that Hitler was opposed to the forced labour of foreign civilians, and Himmler had tried in vain to stop Krupp using children.

Take off. Painting by Dame Laura Knight. A Lancaster leaving
for its target in the Ruhr

He went up to his room in the Krupp guest house, put out the light and pulled back the black-out curtains. A bright glow shone on the western horizon, and he could see the red marker flares from the pathfinder planes poised in space on their parachutes like a grand firework display in slow motion. Mulheim tonight, he thought. Or, perhaps, another big one over at Duisburg. Either way, however, his family at Liebheim would be safely out of it. He lingered for a few minutes, against his will, entranced by the beauty of the sight, then closed the curtains and went to bed. With luck the sirens would not sound their eerie wail again that night.

With the farewells of his family in his ears, John Austin boarded the train for the uncomfortable journey back to his base in East Anglia. Victor Adams, he noticed wryly, was on the same train and on the same mission. Flying Officer Adams, however, was travelling first class, and Flight Sergeant Austin was in third. The coincidence of their meeting at the flying training school in Rhodesia, and finishing up together in 617 Squadron, always struck him as too odd to be untrue. There was Victor as large as life, a fully fledged pilot with a Distinguished Flying Cross and fifty trips over Germany behind him, while John, because of his high technical abilities, had been given no chance to fly the planes: he was ideal navigator material, they said, and that was that.

Both of them, in their different ways, had selected themselves. Wing Commander Guy Gibson had included them when he assembled this squadron of Bomber Command's élite for a secret mission calling for the utmost in ability and daring. Despite the secrecy, they had gathered that they were to have some sort of superbomb, a weapon that might knock the stuffing out of the enemy in one well-aimed blow.

The 48-hour leave just finishing had been a breathing space after the toughest assignment they'd ever had – two months of flying their Lancaster bombers at a height of 20 metres over a lake and dropping a cunningly shaped dummy bomb so that it bounced along the surface as if a giant were skimming a huge pebble over the water. Dr Barnes Wallis, the scientist who'd thought up the stunt, stood by the edge of the lake. When the bombs bounced as he had planned, they could see him running round and round like an excited schoolboy.

By mid April they could do this with precision every time, so Gibson now gave them the same task to do by moonlight. As the altimeters were not accurate enough, they fixed two spotlights on the wing tips so that their beams intersected 20 metres below the aircraft. All they had to do was to fly on an even keel keeping the single spot of light flashing along on the water, imagining all the time that guns were blazing at them from every side.

Tonight the game would be for real.

The briefing was short and efficient. Nineteen of Bomber Command's best aircrews, on their toes with excitement, discovered that their targets for the night were five big dams at the eastern edge of the Ruhr. The huge Möhne dam had first priority, followed by the dam of the River Eder. Models of each structure were closely examined. They were divided into three flights, one starting out due east, then turning southwards at the Zuider Zee, while the other two would take a more southerly route, arriving finally on the same approach to the Möhne dam. The whole trip across the North Sea, Holland and Germany was to be flown at a height of only 30 metres. Their star turn at flying and precision bombing at such ridiculously low levels, the young Australian navigator 'Mick' Martin, gave them a quick run down on the key points of his technique.

After the briefing, John walked out on the moonlit tarmac. The bombs, like giant footballs, were already loaded, and the silence of the fens around the remote airfield split apart as the Merlin engines of Guy Gibson's aircraft sprang one by one into life. Gibson nursed his Merlins like babies. He always managed to fix a little extra fuel so that he could given them more time to warm up. Victor Adams and John followed in the third flight, to back up the Möhne and Eder attacks if necessary and, if not, to go on to the other dams.

According to plan, they crossed the coast south of Lowestoft and flew above the foam-flecked waves of the North Sea. Soon they would be picked up by the coastal radar on the Scheldt, but John knew that ahead of them lay several hundred mixed bombers – Lancs, Wimpeys and Halifaxes. That should divert the attention of the defenders from the tiny squadron, soon to split off for its precision operation. Already the pathfinders would be dropping their marker flares, like slowly falling Christmas trees, bringing a weird daylight to one of the Ruhr cities to the south of their route. With luck, the German nightfighter force for 16-17 May would be on its way there.

In the moments when he wasn't calculating, plotting and adjusting their course, John thought of the operation as the climax to his tour of operations. Since January he had been frequently to Germany, a dozen times to the Ruhr. Those trips took him down Flak Alley, so-called by the aircrews because of the fire from the Flug-AbwehrKannonen, the Krupp anti-aircraft guns that seemed to be as thick on the ground as spectators at a football match.

For a while he had thought of himself as an avenging angel, thrilling to Churchill's promise: 'Germany will be subjected to an ordeal the like of which has never been experienced by a country in continuity, severity, and magnitude.' But he had learned what that really meant. When his target had been given as 'the town hall at the centre of Cologne', or 'the south-western suburbs of Essen' – the residential suburbs away from any of the Krupp works – the message had started to sink in. Still, the high spirits of his companions, many of them idealistic youngsters with the freshness of schoolboys about them, dispelled his thoughts.

Anyway, tonight was different. These vast dams, they'd been told, were crucial to the German war effort. The models in their intensive training sessions, showing the exact location of the anti-torpedo nets, proved how seriously the enemy regarded them. But brains would beat brawn. Breaching the dams would be a huge blow to German morale. Disrupting communications and causing general havoc in that vital region was expected to bring a dramatic shortening of the war. John's nerves tingled in anticipation.

Eight of the nine planes that set out on the first flight met at the rendezvous, and they set course for the Möhne. John's pilot had seen a bomber going down in flames ahead of them as they crossed the heavily defended Dutch coastline. He worked out that it was probably Victor Adams, but their special high-frequency intercoms were strictly reserved for commands or emergencies, and until they got back they would only be able to wonder which of their comrades had gone . . .

Soon there was no time to wonder about anything. With their heavy load, they were circling very slowly, and John was working flat out to keep his course plotting on time. Somewhere in his mind a picture formed of Guy Gibson's dark Lancaster as the spear point of their strung out formation, swooping in like an eagle through the patches of mist rising from the valley. With no need for an oxygen mask at this low altitude, Guy would be singing aloud his favourite bombing song, the Ride of the Valkyries, rising above the scream of the straining Merlins as they closed in on their target.

Precisely according to plan, the huge birds bounced their eggs along the placid waters of the Möhne dam, over the helpless anti-torpedo nets, and into its vast concrete walls. All you had to do was to get the height, speed and time exactly right and avoid the murderous flak that was being thrown up by what seemed to be a thousand 88 millimetre batteries clustered round the dam.

Gibson's bomb was perfectly placed. It threw a white plume of water up into the moonlight, bounced and exploded against the concrete parapet. The wall held. His plane banked into a slow circle, strafing the gun emplacements and searchlights and drawing fire away from the second Lancaster now making its run up. Before it could release its bomb, it was struck by a rain of cannon shells. It rolled over and crashed with a violent explosion on top of the power house behind the dam.

Three more planes made perfect approaches, and their bombs burst accurately on the wall. Still it held. Then, as Gibson was turning again, he heard an excited voice on the intercom: 'She's gone! she's gone!'

Below him the lake was surging wildly in the moonlight, and as they turned he could see that it was pouring out through a gaping breach in the wall. He straightened out and sped the giant bomber down the valley. Climbing back from their nearly suicidal level of 20 metres, he stared with strange fascination at the glimpses he could catch through the rising mist. He saw the headlights of a car speeding away from the oncoming wave. As he looked, the lights became a pale blue, then green, then dark purple, and then there were only the waves and the water.

An hour later, five of the surviving Lancasters repeated the performance 80 kilometres away on the River Eder. None was unscathed. Only one reached the third vital target, the Sorpe dam, and its single bomb was not enough to breach that massive structure. The bombers limping home had to face the ordeal of Flak Alley yet again; they had not enough fuel to get back any other way even though the Junkers 88s would certainly be there hunting for them. Eleven of the nineteen Lancasters eventually got back, two with their tail gunners shot into shreds.

As they soared away from the dam, with shells, tracer bullets and searchlights blazing around them, they took in the unforgettable sight of the frothing waters gushing from the gaps. The night was too dark to follow the millions of tonnes of water cascading down the valley, carrying away men and women, babies and animals, and drowning everything standing on the river banks, such as the little village of Liebheim.

Back again in their Lincolnshire base, the bomber crews were too elated to go to bed as usual. Instead they threw a party which lasted the whole day. While this was in full swing the equally elated Sir Archibald Sinclair, Minister of Air, was making an announcement. 'I have great news for you,' he said. 'Two of the greatest dams in Germany have been breached by our bombers. The water descended through the Ruhr valley in huge waves. Eight of our planes were lost.'

News of the daring exploit sped round the world. In Melbourne the *Age* showed a picture of the waters cascading through the 60 metre gap in the Möhne wall, with headlines:

DISASTER STRIKES GERMANY:
Death and Destruction in Dam Attack;
Reports from Berne – 4000 killed and 120 000 homeless

The next day, the flooding of fifty-four towns and villages was reported. Amid rain, hail, and freezing temperatures, the refugees were camping out on high ground while the waters kept rising. 'A major victory' was the official description of the action.

The irrepressible human spirit kept revealing itself. Mick Martin received a letter from Australia asking for a souvenir of the raid: he sent a reply saying that he was enclosing the Möhne dam for their museum. On the envelope, in red ink, his gunner wrote, 'Opened by censors and the contents confiscated by the Metropolitan Water Board.'

Nor was the humour confined solely to the 'victors'. At the dam, the commander of the defences, Hauptmann Freisewinkel, was more than a little disturbed by the raid. About 500 Germans, 700 foreign workers in a labour camp, and 1000 cattle had died. It took him over a year to get it repaired and to strengthen the defences. 'The next time the dam is attacked,' he said ruefully, 'I shall be rewarded either with the Knight's Cross or with the guillotine.'

For John it was several weeks before the full realization of that heroic night sank in, and much longer before he found out that the effect on the war potential of the Reich was minute. He began to

Dambusting. The Möhne dam, before and after, 16 May 1943

take more seriously the criticisms by dissident military authorities: General Fuller, for example, decrying 'the massacre of civilian populations'. But no regrets or denunciations could bring back the little family of Manfred Schiller.

Five years later, in the dock at Nuremburg, Alfried Krupp would be the cool and collected general of industry. Yes, he had used foreign labour. Yes, he had used Jews from the concentration camps; that was doing his bounden duty to the fatherland. No, he didn't know of any particularly bad conditions. Conditions were bad for everyone at the time. He had been much too busy to notice such minor incidents as two young Polish boys, beaten and half-starved, being deliberately worked to their deaths in his arms factory.

To be fair to Krupp, however, the last two years had been bad. In the midsummer of 1943, Hitler had ordered a desperate counter-offensive to cut off the advancing Russian armies in the salient at Kursk. Grudgingly, he had been persuaded to call back the great Guderian as Inspector General of Armoured Troops. At once the general began to criticize the mess that Krupps had made of tank production. Their two fancy sports car designers, Ferdinand and Ferry Porsche, had let their imaginations run riot with tanks of all shapes and sizes up to a thousand tonnes. Ferry Porsche had previously distinguished himself by designing a people's car, the Volkswagen. Mass-produced from steel pressings, with a simple air-cooled engine, it was to be a triumph of Nazism for the people. The design of the car had pleased Hitler, even if the people didn't get any. But the tank department was in poor shape. On 5 July, when Hitler ordered the attack, Krupp's tanks received a knock-out blow: in military circles it is still known as 'The Death Ride of the Panzers'.

Over the fortnight that the Kursk battle raged, the Soviet armour proved overwhelmingly superior to that of Krupps. Hitler had thrown in seventeen armoured divisions. It was nearly all he had, and he almost lost them all. Three-quarters of the German tanks and self-propelled guns were destroyed, and 70 000 German soldiers lay dead. The battle stands as the greatest clash of steel armour in the history of warfare: it was the beginning of the end for Hitler.

It also marked the fall of the leading merchants of death, Krupps, the steel and cannon kings. Thenceforth steel would become the best supporting actor in a war game where the stars are more sophisticated products of science – the jet planes and aircraft carriers, radar and guidance systems, intercontinental ballistic missiles, nuclear weapons, submarines, and satellites. And these would be the products of a new generation of death merchants. In Anthony Sampson's hair-raising account of the post-war arms business, *The Arms Bazaar*, the names of the old merchants, the Krupps, Schneiders and Vickers, are dwarfed by the merchants of high-technological death, the Lockheeds, the Aerospatiales, and the General Dynamics.

Those who observed the impassive Alfried Krupp sitting under guard through the war crimes trial in 1948 were struck by the remoteness of this stiff and isolated figure, one of the world's richest and most powerful men. Had his training so conditioned him that he could exclude all trace of common humanity in his pursuit of power and profit? Had he become as subhuman as he believed his captive workers from the east to be? Was he incapable of responding to the humanity that continually burst through the darkest scenes of war, such as that recounted by the poet Yevgeny Yevtushenko from the time in Moscow when Siegfried Schiller's tank squadron was drawing close?

They were people! German prisoners approaching Moscow,
1943

In '41 Mama took me back to Moscow. There I saw our enemies for the first
time. If my memory is right, nearly twenty thousand German war prisoners
were to be marched in a single column through the streets of Moscow.

The pavements swarmed with onlookers, cordoned off by soldiers and
police.

The crowd were mostly women – Russian women with hands rough-
ened by hard work, lips untouched by lipstick and thin hunched shoulders
which had borne half the burden of the war. Every one of them must have
had a father or a husband, a brother or a son killed by the Germans.

They gazed with hatred in the direction from which the column was to
appear.

At last we saw it.

The generals marched at the head, massive chins stuck out, lips folded
disdainfully, their whole demeanour meant to show superiority over their
plebeian victors.

'They smell of eau-de-cologne, the bastards', someone in the crowd said
with hatred.

The women were clenching their fists. It was all that the soldiers and
policemen could do to hold them back.

All at once something happened to them.

They saw German soldiers, thin, unshaven, wearing dirty blood-stained bandages, hobbling on crutches or leaning on the shoulders of their comrades; the soldiers walked with their heads down.

The street became dead silent – the only sound was the shuffling of boots and the thumping of crutches.

Then I saw an elderly woman in broken-down boots push herself forward and touch a policeman's shoulder saying: 'Let me through.' There must have been something about her that made him step aside.

She went up to the column, took from inside her coat something wrapped in a coloured handkerchief and unfolded it. It was a crust of black bread. She pushed it awkwardly into the pocket of a soldier, so exhausted that he was tottering on his feet. And now suddenly from every side women were running towards the soldiers, pushing into their hands bread, cigarettes, whatever they had.

The soldiers were no longer enemies.

They were people.

TWENTY-THREE

The Twilight of the Krupps

The race of gods passed away like a breath: without a ruler I leave the world behind, but I bequeath to it the treasure of my divine wisdom; neither goods nor gold; neither divine glory, nor lordly state ... sublime in sorrow and in joy, let Love reign alone!

The Twilight of the Gods

Tramping through the broken glass and smoking rubble of an Essen street, Baldur Schiller tried to put out of his mind the death of his son on the eastern front. It would help if he concentrated on the managerial meeting ahead of him. Alfried would preside as usual. After the extent of the night's damage had been reported, he would select the appropriate emergency plan, involving such fine points as organizing the mobile staircases that would be wheeled into place to keep the partially destroyed factories going.

It was this attention to detail that enabled the Ruhr to keep increasing its output through the long months of the strategic bombing. Replicas of the complex network of points and junctions that made up the marshalling yards at Hamm were assembled in the country, ready to be brought in as soon as a raid ended. RAF Mosquitoes reconnoitring the next day found it difficult to recognize the fully operational junction from the flash photographs brought home by the bombers. Although thousands of workers had been killed or wounded, the bombing offensive was proving a costly failure.

The gaunt steelmaster had shown that his nerves were as hard as his steel. He would pace the rooms of his lonely castle while the Lancasters droned above, or sit by his fireside with a bottle of Scotch and several packs of Camel cigarettes. Alone, save for his army of servants, he pondered the future of a Ruhr industrialist as he changed the gramophone record from *Siegfried* to its sequel, *The Twilight of the Gods*.

He would have needed a very superior crystal ball to reveal such unlikely visions as a revolution in the methods of warfare, the decline of the steel industry, or the fall of the House of Krupp. Yet all of these became probable within the next five years and certain within forty.

The meeting went as smoothly as Baldur Schiller had expected. But as 1944 wore on he had new problems to worry about. There was, for example, the concentration camp at Buchmannshof. Built by Krupp well away from the town, it housed a number of sickly infants, none more than three years old. These were the babies conceived by women slave-workers who were given a few weeks off when the babies were born and then sent back to the factory. According to the joke, it had not been necessary to surround the camp with barbed wire.

And now Krupp had loaded him with a new and heavy task. As in boardrooms all over Europe, the Krupp managers knew that the end of the war was in sight and had begun to lay plans for the aftermath. Already secrets were being withheld from allies and friends: very soon they might become commercial enemies.

Baldur's job was harder than most: building up the financial reserves where they would be out of reach of the Nazi party. His task was interrupted by the news that his younger son, Manfred, had been shot for conspiring to kill the führer. In the gruelling inquisitions that followed, he had a double problem: to demonstrate his own innocence without revealing that he was spending most of his time hiding funds from the Nazis.

On the battlefields of Europe, Germany was beginning to fall under the sheer weight of steel. Allied production of tanks outnumbered the German by six to one. It was the old story of the Hittites: many cheap iron swords overcoming a few high-quality bronze.

But already the power of war was no longer to be measured simply in units of brute force, millions of men or tonnes of steel. Science was moving into the lead. Strange propellerless aircraft zoomed through the skies at unbelievable speed; battlefields on land, sea, or in the air, were surveyed by the invisible beams of radar. At Hitler's desperate command, the secret weapons V1 and V2 launched their terrorist attacks upon London. Soviet tanks advancing by night to liberate Warsaw were hit by German guns using infra-red sights to see them in the dark. The carefully planned fire-storm bombing of Dresden demonstrated how to turn a whole city into a bonfire. And, like the climax to some diabolical fireworks show, the seal was set on the new era of scientific warfare when a few kilograms of refined uranium or plutonium were shot together to blow the hearts out of two Japanese cities.

In 1948 the gaunt steelmaster was once more sitting and pondering his future in the Landsberg prison where a quarter of a century earlier Hitler had sat writing *Mein Kampf*. In the Nuremberg Palace of Justice, Krupp had listened impassively to his sentence: 'Imprisonment for twelve years and forfeiture of all of your property, both real and personal.' Was this the end of the dynasty of Krupp, the last sorry chapter of a century and a half's world leadership in armaments and steel?

Within three years, Alfried Krupp was out of prison. Two years later he was the foremost industrialist in Europe, and in another five he had become one of the richest men in the world. In 1967 he built Germany's first atomic reactor using uranium from the US Atomic Energy Commission. It may have been a tribute to the magical new process of generating electricity, but when the reactor was named Merlin it seemed more to signify the wizardry of Krupp's recovery.

It was not magic, however, that had saved him: it was the cold war. Germany arose like a phoenix from its ashes. The Russians and the French wanted to keep Germany permanently divided; one had lost twenty million dead, and the other had memories of carnage stretching back to the Franco-Prussian war. Britain and America felt that total demilitarization would suffice. As the ideological rift between East and West widened, Krupp slipped neatly through the gap.

During the Berlin blockade, the airlift and the partition of Germany, the United States became infected by McCarthyism. When the Korean war erupted, China and the Soviet Union were held to be the common enemy and West Germany was promoted as a bulwark against the universal spectre of communism.

In 1951 the US General John J. McCloy ordered the premature release of Krupp and was outraged at the protests that resounded across Europe. He need not have worried. Clement Attlee, the British Prime Minister, defended McCloy's action, saying: 'There is no question of Krupp being allowed to assume either ownership or control of the former Krupp industrial empire.' Indeed there was no question: he was allowed to and he did.

Over the next fifteen years Krupp's progress was spectacular. Soon the Krupp products selling around the world ranged from false teeth to a complete steel factory using the oxygen-blowing process that was the ultimate form of Henry Bessemer's original converter. Alfried Krupp sold that factory as a package deal to Pandit Nehru for $150 million. It included a town for the workers to live in, with its own park, hotel, housing, car-free shopping centre and surrounding autobahn. It was a miniature Essen.

Although he also sold railway locos, lorries, bridges, paper mills and cement plants to Egypt, Turkey, Brazil, Japan, Mexico, Canada and several African countries, the basis of it all was high-quality Krupp steel. 'The cobbler must stick to his last', Krupp told his dynamic manager, Berthold Beitz. 'Our future lies in producing the special steels needed for modern high-grade machinery.' Beitz agreed. He could sell that concept to the world, counting on the reputation of German science and technology to support the products of the Ruhr against their age-old rival, Sheffield. Domestically there would never be any problems. 'Hart wie Kruppstahl' had become a national catchcry ever since the führer had shouted at the Hitler Youth: 'Be tough as leather, swift as whippets, and hard as Krupp steel.'

Special steels were the delight of Dr Henry Lovedale. Resisting all inducements to go into the family business, he had taken a research degree at his university for the sheer joy of studying the changes in metals that could be brought about by subtle additions of other elements. Special steels he found particularly fascinating, and the success of his research on these alloys had brought him a lectureship in metallurgy. He would describe them to his astonished students at Sheffield University as the paragons of metals, sublime in every feature. Unlike aluminium, he would say, age would not harden them, nor custom stale their infinite variety.

He always began his course with a story about Lord Nelson. Not about his flagship, the *Victory*, which was made of wood, but about its cast-iron guns, which went on firing after the French guns on the

Redoubtable had burst. The English barrels, he said, were thicker, heavier and tightly bound with wire to reduce the chance of a burst and a mangled heap of gunlayers and gunpowder boys to swab off the deck. But the question was: why did these hard, iron barrels burst?

Henry Lovedale would produce a photograph showing the structure of ordinary cast iron. He would point to the dark, squiggly lines, which he said were the carbon in the iron formed into thin flakes of graphite. 'The sharp edges of these flakes weaken the metal,' he would say, and then pick on a student to explain why this was so.

On this occasion, in 1967, earlier lectures on the strength of materials flashed through the student's mind. Grasping at an answer, he proposed 'Dislocations!' elaborating this cryptic declaration by explaining that each graphite flake disrupts the nicely ordered planes of atoms in the iron. 'When the explosion puts the iron under tension, one row of atoms flips across the gap created by the sharp edge of the graphite flake, leaving a space for the next row to flip into, and so on, until the barrel cracks right through. This needs far less tension than would be needed to break the pure iron without any of these disrupting carbon flakes.'

'Not a bad guess,' conceded Henry, 'but the dark recesses of your mind have come up with the answer to a different question. You've told us why a ductile metal like mild steel deforms plastically when the stress becomes too great. The question before us is why a brittle material, such as glass or cast iron, doesn't deform but shatters. 'How about you, Fei Ma?' he asked. 'Why does a cast-iron gun barrel burst?' 'Is it because the sharp edges of the graphite flakes concentrate the stress?' Han Fei Ma suggested, as casually as she could. 'Like the example we had of a crack in a glass. Any force on the glass gets magnified at the tip of the crack so that it splits apart quite easily. Isn't it a case of Griffith's theory of brittle fracture?'

'At least someone has been listening,' sighed Henry. 'Now this will show you what a proper grasp of the science of materials can do. It has recently been found that the shape of these graphite inclusions can be changed from thin flakes into little balls, by adding a tiny amount of magnesium to the liquid iron before it's poured into the mould. Less than a twentieth of a per cent is enough.'

He continued, 'When this spheroidal graphite cast iron is put into tension it extends by about 10 per cent before it breaks, and its breaking strength is several times greater than that of ordinary grey cast iron. This tough material can be cast into complicated shapes – an engine crankshaft, for instance – saving all that expensive forging, rolling, machining and balancing.'

'Now,' he went on, 'I promised to tell you something about the research projects for next year. They're all concerned with special steels. I know it's only a small part of steel production, but it's an area of growing importance, and it's one place where Sheffield still leads the world. Ordinary mild steel isn't very exciting, and aluminium and plastics are starting to replace it for many purposes. So the fascination's going to be in studying things like the influence of grain size on the latest idea, high strength, low alloy steels.'

As Lovedale hoped, this caused a stir at the back of the class. He went on to elaborate. 'These high strength, low alloy steels, for those of you who haven't been keeping up with the literature, are really normal low-carbon steels with the addition of small amounts of alloying elements. Adding only a few tenths of a per cent of manganese and silicon, for instance, gives a much finer grain size to the metal, increasing its strength and improving other mechanical properties. These steels are going to be very valuable for making complicated parts in machinery and cars. There's a lot of fundamental work to be done, but there'll also be many applications and some good jobs to go with them.'

At the time that Henry Lovedale was seducing his students with the delights of special steels, the House of Krupp was beginning to look more like a House of Cards. West Germany was in its deepest recession since the war, and Krupp was in financial trouble. Its bank debts alone exceeded two billion dollars.

Without a kaiser or a führer standing behind it, Krupp's private empire was vulnerable to that curious institution known as the financial system. When a debt grows large enough, the bankers cannot afford to let the borrower go bankrupt. The standard way out, as with huge loans to a developing country, is to put in more money and at the same time impose a political solution to the problems. That is what happened to Alfried Krupp. His firm was converted into a corporation, to be run by a council. After 31 January 1968, the senior male Krupp would no longer be in the sole control of Messrs Friedrich Krupp of Essen. 'Probably the greatest sensation in German industrial history since the war', commented *Izvestia*.

Of the many ironies in this collapse, the first was that Krupp had depended too much upon steel. It was steel that carried Alfred Krupp to his throne as Cannon King; it was the declining fortunes of steel that brought his great-grandson down. The steel and coal interests – which, under Allied Law 27, Alfried was actually forbidden to hold – were responsible for over half his losses in 1966. He had not only illegally regained the holdings, but had also been busily enlarging them. With a strong sense of loyalty to his workers, social responsibility as he saw it, he had invested $300 million in items such as a modern hot strip mill, at a time when the industry was already heading for over-capacity. For similar sentimental reasons he maintained the traditional production of Krupp locomotives, unprofitable though it might be.

Perhaps someone, someday, may construct a plausible version of the bluffs and double-bluffs that led to the final catastrophe. The central figure in this story is not Krupp but his ebullient go-getting general manager, Bertholt Beitz.

The fall and rise of Bertholt Beitz seemed as dramatic and as irresistible as that of Alfried Krupp. In 1940 he was in charge of oil production for the German government in Poland. Such was his skill that he ran the oil business to his masters' satisfaction while saving countless Poles from the gas chambers and helping members of the Resistance to escape the Gestapo's clutches.

In 1945, with his parents, wife and young children, he was living a hand-to-mouth existence in a hut near Hamburg. Getting a toehold in the insurance business was enough for this agile entrepreneur to rise to the top. Brashness and brilliance brought him to a private dinner with Krupp. The encounter was so successful that Krupp offered him the job of running his whole industrial empire, although the ultimate power would stay with Krupp. And as befitted the richest industrialist in Europe, the salary of his number one assistant would also be the highest in Europe.

Beitz was the perfect complement to Krupp. Where Krupp followed the nineteenth-century tradition established by the old Cannon King, Beitz followed no tradition. Where Krupp played his tapes of Wagner, Beitz played Dixieland. But where Krupp saw an opening for profit, ahead of all his rivals, there the difference disappeared: Beitz was as keen as his master. And that was where the trouble began.

Faced with Krupp's refusal to get out of the coal and steel business, Beitz turned to the East. His unorthodox wartime experience in occupied Poland came to his advantage. With the flair that had brought him the rare friendship of Germany's leading industrialist, he was soon on good terms with Anastas Mikoyan, the dapper Armenian who ran the Soviet trade department, with Richard Nixon, and with Otto Brenner, President of the Metalworkers Union. A warm relationship with Nikita Khrushchev blossomed, yielding a roaring trade not only with Russia but also with Poland, Rumania, Czechoslovakia, Hungary, Bulgaria, and Yugoslavia. China also came in with a $150 million order for a complete Krupp steelworks.

Chancellor Konrad Adenauer was among those who were not amused. 'Why not wear a red carnation in your buttonhole, Herr Beitz?' he enquired. But Alfried came instantly to the defence of his lieutenant. Recalling the role of his great-grandfather during the creation of the German state, he pronounced that selling goods in the East had nothing whatever to do with politics; their real concern was making jobs for German workmen.

Sales continued to mount. European competitors moved in on this lucrative market, but Beitz kept Krupp in the lead by cutting prices and offering long-term – sometimes very long-term – payments. So it was that in the 1967 recession, Krupp had long lines of credit but no ready cash to meet his commitments. The jaws of the financial establishment closed inexorably around him. The largest private industrial empire in history had reached the end of the road.

What really happened? Did the two smartest businessmen in Germany fail to understand the difference between short-term and long-term credit? Had 300 German banks abandoned the homage due to a Krupp – a name that had come to mean more to them than a Beethoven, a Goethe or a Wagner, a family that had worked with and outlasted kaisers, chancellors and führers? Or had Krupp been crushed by the embrace of the Russian bear, a sweet revenge for the guns that had slain millions?

Was there an unseen American hand in the downfall, a final twist from Washington after Krupp had refused to withhold the steelworks from China, which was sending tanks and guns into Vietnam?

And what was the role of Bertholt Beitz, the flamboyant Americanophile businessman and friend of Khrushchev?

We may never know. But what might have happened if Krupp's only son Arndt had not been the man he was, the self-appointed playboy of the Western world?

Just as Alfried had looked to his great-grandfather Alfred as a guiding light, so Arndt had tried to look at his own great-grandfather, Fritz. He saw a man frustrated by the burden of the family tradition, striving to carry on as head of the House of Krupp and snatching only brief Mediterranean interludes to do what he really wanted. For what? asked Arndt, and came to his own conclusion.

Alfried Krupp's funeral on 30 July 1967 took place at the family graveyard in Essen. 'I am not a man like my father,' said Arndt, 'who sacrifices his whole life for something, not knowing whether it is really worth it in our time.' He decided that life in the house on that cold, northern hill in Germany had little appeal compared with life on the Isle of Capri and even less when compared with his own estate in Brazil.

Arndt had ostensibly acquired this country seat as a handy base for his business operations. Krupp's largest overseas enterprise was the Brazilian factory at Campo Limpo. It was built on a converted coffee plantation and dedicated to making axle forgings for heavy lorries, which would be thundering in increasing numbers along the trans-Amazon highway as the sleeping giant of Latin America awoke to its true potential. Arndt found it, in practice, much handier to the Copacabana beach at Rio, or for a trip in his latest sports car round the mountainous circuit of south-eastern Brazil. When he felt like some city life, he could pack his Rolls in the hold of his plane and fly down to São Paulo, the largest city in the southern hemisphere, with its sophisticated cabarets and night clubs.

This, Arndt decided, was the life. A whirl of exciting parties, with exciting partners, such as the beautiful ex-queen Soraya of Iran, Hildegarde Neff, or Gina Lollobrigida. To the devil with 'Krupp'; Arndt von Bohlen und Halbach he was and would remain. Only if Alfried named him as his successor would he have been entitled, by the Lex Krupp Act of 1943, governing the ownership of the great firm, to use the name of Krupp. But, on 1 April 1967, control of the firm had passed to a council, and Alfried Krupp had died without naming a successor. In any case, it was clear that Arndt just wasn't interested.

Arndt von Bohlen hits the headlines: 'Krupp heir robbed in luxury hotel!'

The things that Arndt was interested in would need a regular and substantial supply of cash. So his loving father had carefully drawn up a deed compensating Arndt for the loss of his 'rights'. Messrs Krupp accordingly have to pay him, as a first charge, ahead of any dividends, half a million dollars a year for the rest of his life. That's $10 000 a week pocket money for the jet-setting playboy.

And the act on which the whole arrangement rested, the Lex Krupp, is an act authorized and signed by an old family friend, Adolf Hitler.

TWENTY-FOUR

Kruppism Lives!

When the next war's over, it will be the electronics firms and the missile manufacturers who will be put in the dock before a war crimes tribunal, not us.

Bertholt Beitz

Bertholt Beitz was an optimist as well as a humorist. Optimist to imagine that the survivors of World War III would be able to organize their own survival, never mind a war crimes tribunal; humorist to suggest that the Krupp industrial empire was not contributing, at least indirectly, to the electronics and missiles of modern warfare. One subsidiary, for instance, was making jet fighters in association with the Pratt and Whitney engine manufacturer, United Aircraft.

But in a modern society every industry directly or indirectly contributes to its weaponry. By the 1960s Krupps were now no more culpable than anyone else: they were still kings of steel; but their primary concern lay in peaceful production. Although their range of products stretched from abattoirs to zirconium, they still remembered the Old Steelmaker's precept: stick to your last. And the heart of Krupps had always been steel.

The Bessemer converters and the open hearth furnaces had all gone. In their place stood huge, tilting, pear-shaped vessels, looking not unlike the old Bessemers and lined with refractory material, just as specified by Sidney Gilchrist Thomas a century ago. To operate one of these new monsters, it was charged with molten pig iron, and pure oxygen was blown on to the liquid metal through a water-cooled lance only a few centimetres above its surface.

The liquid iron seethed furiously. Great clouds of brown and orange fumes emerged, adding their colourful contribution to the skies over Essen or Rheinhausen; those were the days before pollution control became a matter for legislation. Within an hour, from start to finish, the excess carbon had been burned out of the iron and a hundred tonnes of steel were ready for pouring.

This basic oxygen steelmaking process was a simple step in technological evolution. Henry Bessemer had patented the idea long ago, but it could not become a practical proposition until gas lique-faction techniques had brought down the price of oxygen to an industrial level. The process was both fast and economical. Moreover the oxygen produced so much heat that a third of the charge could consist of scrap steel. This was a valuable bonus for the Krupp factories throughout Germany: it was easier now to recycle their large stocks of this 'waste' product.

The speed of the process demanded modern high technology to control it. Although most of the impurities were bound into a slag by the added lime, some remained, and the actual composition of the molten steel was uncertain. In the old open hearth days, there was time to take samples, analyse them and make suitable additions to the melt. With the whole process over in less than an hour, com-puterized instruments had to be developed to give an analysis in a matter of minutes. Materials could then be added to bring the steel to the exact composition required.

Another sign of Krupp vitality that pleased Bertholt Beitz was the increased size of the electric arc furnaces. They were now producing mild steel from steel scrap by the tonne and were no longer reserved simply for small batches of special alloy steels. Several tonnes of scrap were placed in the furnace together with slag-forming materials. An arc struck between carbon electrodes became so fierce that local spots exceeded the temperature of the surface of the sun; this fused the charge and kept it molten while it combined with the fluxes and other added materials.

Alfried Krupp had used his firm's steelmaking ability as one of his weapons in the battle to regain his steel empire in the 1950s. He won the battle, although eventually it lost him the war. Through a quixotic sense of family loyalty to his workers, he had striven to regain his vast coal and steel enterprises, but when both coal and steel ran into hard times the losses were greater than even the finances of Krupp could bear.

While Alfried Krupp was trying hard to lose all connections with warfare, Bertholt Beitz was more positive: he saw no future in war-fare at all. He observed, with some satisfaction, that traditional Krupp lines, like big guns and battleships, were now obsolete. 'If the continent were threatened by an arms race,' he remarked, 'we should get hold of Schneider-Creusot, Vickers-Armstrong, and Skoda, and say, "Hello, let's have a drink and sit down and see if we can't do something better than make guns".'

No longer are Krupps the Merchants of Death. Like a reformed drunk refusing a lemon shandy, they do not even allow toy guns or soldiers to be sold in their modern supermarkets.

The old arms pushers have gone, like the old steel converters, but, just as in the steel mills, new and improved models have taken their place: Sam Cummings, for instance, probably the world's leading dealer in private arms. Showing Anthony Sampson round his Manchester warehouse in 1976, Cummings explained how the 300 000 weapons he had on display had been recycled through Germany, Greece, Vietnam, Taiwan, France, Venezuela, Egypt, Jordan, Chile, and the Philippines. Some had been owned by Hitler or by Chiang Kai-shek; some by the British, the Japanese or the Israelis; some by the French Maquis. To the twentieth-century armourer, guns are the real currency of the world.

Cummings is, in the fashionable term, a realist. That means that he has abandoned the old-fashioned ideas of principles; he is dispassionately cynical: there is none of the patriotic hypocrisy of his forerunners. 'The arms business,' he told Sampson, 'is founded on human folly. That is why its depths will never be plumbed, and why it will go on forever.' Adding sarcasm to cynicism he went on: 'All weapons are defensive, and all spare parts are non-lethal.'

Even in 1935 Lloyd George was arguing before the 1935 Royal Commission that the private manufacture of arms is intolerable in a civilized, peace-loving state. But one's natural revulsion should not get the situation out of perspective. Cummings and all of his kind added together account for less than a twentieth part of the world's arms traffic. The arms pushers that really matter today are to be found among senior public servants, military officers, ministers of government, royal princes, and the chiefs of the aerospace business.

The corruption and double-dealing at all levels is the subject matter of many lurid adventure paperbacks, mostly falling far short of the reality. Senator Frank Church, chairman of the US Senate subcommittee looking into the industry's influence upon foreign policy, must have read some particularly good ones. 'This sordid tale of bribery,' he said in 1975, 'has a cast of characters out of a novel of international intrigue.' It says a lot for the arms business that he was still able to be astonished, even after investigating ITT's involvement in Chile. The arms race, he warned, was out of control.

But the cruellest and ultimately most sinister aspect of this blossoming arms race was the deception that armament is necessary to create jobs. Not that this was a new idea. Kaiser Wilhelm used it to attack the young peace movement eighty years ago. But it has become more and more strident since World War II, distorting the foreign policies of Western governments, especially where aerospace companies are located in marginal constituencies. It has become one of the main causes of the Cold War and the threats to peace.

In 1965 the British government pulled off a spectacular coup, selling planes and missiles to Saudi Arabia and snatching the order from under the nose of the world's biggest arms company. It was the largest export order in British history, and it meant a lot of well-paid jobs in the British Aircraft works at Warton – touching two marginal constituencies. The guiding spirit was a young, idealistic Labour MP, John Stonehouse. In the process of winning the order, he had been baptized in the corruption that prevails in big business. 'What was the point in adopting a holier-than-thou attitude when Britain's factories sorely needed the business?' he asked in a letter to *The Times* on 2 July 1976.

At a personal level, this young idealist proved unable to cope with his exposure to the wicked world of arms deals. He entered into some unsuccessful private ventures, got into debt and disappeared in Miami, USA, leaving his clothes in a heap on the beach. Eventually he was discovered living under an assumed name in Melbourne, Australia. At his trial he was found guilty of fraud and forgery and went to jail, a minor casualty of the rough and tough arms trade.

A tougher customer was Marcel Dassault, French aircraft manufacturer, survivor of Buchenwald, and creator of the Mirage jet fighter with its delta wings and rocket boosters. In 1976 the media launched accusations that his military-industrial complex had been guilty of tax avoidance on an outrageous scale. Unruffled, he appeared on Paris television pronouncing himself quite willing to be nationalized, if that was what the country wanted. But, he asked, did they really want another version of their already nationalized and loss-making company, Aerospatiale, a stodgy and inefficient business compared with his own dynamic enterprise?

Dassault survived as a private business, but six years later both

Dassault and Aerospatiale were back in the news again, giving a sharp reminder of what the business was really about.

There was a dispute over the sovereignty of some bleak islands in the South Atlantic, in Britain called the Falklands and in Argentina the Malvinas. In 1914 British cruisers destroyed Admiral von Spee's naval squadron in a battle to prevent him from landing there. Nearly seventy years later, in 1982, the Argentinians landed and occupied the islands. The British responded by sending a task force of 28 000 men to get them out.

David Tinker, a 25-year-old Royal Navy lieutenant on the destroyer HMS *Glamorgan*, sent many letters home during the long journey south and the battle. One recorded a heart-stopping attack by Mirage fighters on May Day. A week later, two Super Etendards came screaming towards the task force. From 40 kilometres distance they let fly their Exocet missiles and turned for home. Super Etendards are naval fighter-bombers built by Dassault; Exocets are the 5 metre long missiles built by Aerospatiale in the charming old town of Bourges, once the capital of fifteenth-century France. They skim the surface of the water at nearly the speed of sound, homing by their own radar on to their target which, in this case, was the destroyer HMS *Sheffield*. One of them made a direct hit.

'It had a devastating effect,' said the Captain. 'It came in at about 2 metres above the water level and, when inside the ship, exploded outwards and upwards.'

The spirit of the sailors was remarkable. Those who couldn't help with the firefighting sat on the foredeck, wrapped in blankets against the cold, singing the Monty Python song, 'Always look on the bright side of life.' After burning for several days, HMS *Sheffield* sank to the bottom of the Atlantic to join countless predecessors in the richest graveyard of maritime wrecks in the world. Ships like Sir Francis Drake's *Marigold* have ended there, victims of the cruel passage round the Horn.

Tinker's next letter was scathing about the naval tactics that led to the loss of the *Sheffield*. He was not aware that HMS *Sheffield*'s computerized radar had detected the oncoming missile in time and successfully identified it as an Exocet. The Royal Navy computers, however, had only been programmed against Soviet missiles: they

Exocets for sale. These highly effective French missiles are also advertised with the astonishing catchphrase: 'Fire and Forget!'

recognized Exocets as 'friendly' and had not given any warning to enable counter-measures to be initiated. The computers were belatedly re-programmed.

By the end of the month, the Argentinians had rigged up a launching platform on the main island to fire off a surface-to-surface version of the Exocet, an operation that the Dassault technicians had declared to be impossible. One was fired at the *Glamorgan*. Their computer now gave the crew forty-five seconds warning of the imminent arrival of an Exocet, and they were able to swing the ship round to point directly at it, thereby narrowing its view of the target. At the same time, metallized plastic strips were fired in the path of the missile, so confusing its radar that it plunged harmlessly into the sea 400 metres ahead.

David Tinker had not been frightened, he wrote, because the whole thing was over so quickly. But he felt sorry for the operations officer sitting in the control room watching the missile coming straight at them. His heart, he'd told them later, almost pounded itself out of its rib cage.

Tinker was also feeling sorry for the brave Argentine soldiers and pilots; for their sake he hoped that Argentina would soon surrender. In an earlier letter he'd quoted Wilfred Owen, the young World War I poet, who also felt sympathy for the opposing soldiers, and who was killed in action just a few days before the war came to an end: 'There'll come a day when men make war on death for lives, not men for flags.'

A fortnight later another land-based Exocet was launched at the *Glamorgan*. This time the missile was not decoyed away by plastic strips and, thanks to the efforts of the crew in swinging the ship round again, it missed the control centre and exploded in the stern. HMS *Glamorgan* was saved, the official report stated with relief, and only thirteen men were lost. One of the thirteen was David Tinker. Two days later the war came to an end.

The story in London in the autumn of 1982 was that the war had been won by the French. Certainly there were customers from the Middle East and Latin America queuing up for Exocet and Roland missiles after their marvellous performance in the battle: the first five Exocets fired, for instance, had sunk two large British ships.

Other hardware, such as that made by British Aerospace, could boast successes, and the vaunted spin-off from war was in evidence, but it was a spin-off that helped the arms manufacturers more than anyone else. Indeed, one of the consequences would simply increase the burden on civil society: ships such as HMS *Ardent* had burst into flames when hit, with their lightweight aluminium superstructures burning furiously. It was back to steel again, to the consternation of the aluminium companies, and to the cost of the public for heavier, dearer, warships.

In June 1982 the Mayor of Archente, M. Henri Perrichon sat in his study looking at a map of the world. Coloured pins showed the countries that had bought missiles from Aerospatiale, the main employer in his region: they marked out Argentina and Iraq, Pakistan and Peru, South Africa and England. Now he was struggling to compose a letter to M. Jacques Mitterrand, brother of the President of France, and a director of Aerospatiale. It was a delicate letter, proposing a scaling down of missile development at a time when employment was the main concern of the townspeople. It urged the case that the mayor himself had helped his union, the General Confederation of Labour, to prepare; that it would make better economic sense to concentrate on projects like the successful Airbus. Such projects are more stable and they create more jobs.

The mayor came to the end of his letter and gazed out of his window, across the lush green fields and the vineyards to the thirteenth-century cathedral of Bourges on the hill in the distance. Strange to think of that old city, through which the Roman legions had marched, still so occupied with warfare. It had started in earnest when Louis Napoleon had moved the arsenal there to Bourges, in the middle of France and beyond the reach of the Prussian army. Yet even that hadn't saved him from the onslaught of Bismarck's troops and their deadly steel guns.

Yes, he thought, it was Krupp with his steel cannon that had started the race off. Already it had cost untold litres of blood. France had suffered through three successive wars: could it survive a fourth? The new Kruppism must be stopped, but how? Who would blow the whistle? And if people's jobs were at stake, who would listen? With a shrug of his shoulders, he signed the letter.

TWENTY-FIVE

The Road to Damascus

And suddenly there shined round about him a light from heaven . . .

And immediately there fell from his eyes scales: and he received sight forthwith.

Acts 9:3,18

The 1980s opened badly for iron and blood. Steel tanks and weapons were in action from Asia and the Middle East to Africa and Central America, submarines hunted warships in the South Pacific, and blood was flowing freely. A sobered steel industry was licking its wounds: it had already lost a third of its production and jobs over the last five years, and it was struggling to plan for an uncertain future.

In America, Europe, Australia and Japan output had turned downwards. In Britain, the home of steel, it was falling calamitously and irreversibly as panic seized the government and the senior management: steelworks were closed down, foundries smashed to pieces, blast furnaces blown up, and the lives of whole communities blighted. By contrast, in Brazil, Korea and Taiwan production was rapidly increasing, an interesting phenomenon though not yet significant on the world scene.

But there were some hopeful signs. Not only in the steel industry, but also in the arms industry and in the science of blood and iron people were taking a new look at the problems. And some of the consequences were astonishing.

Inside the depressed United States steel industry, some people were exploring novel ideas of how to run a steelworks, and they were making very high profits. A shining example was the Nucor Corporation. Originally the Nuclear Corporation of America, this company changed its name after it decided to quit the nuclear game and take up the challenge of making steel. It soon became an exemplar of the flexibility of capitalism.

First of all it shunned the giant integrated plants of the major producers and installed instead 'mini-mills', using electric arc furnaces with a capacity between a quarter and a half a million tonnes a year. A 'mini-steelworks' needs less capital per tonne than a conventional steelworks, and it is simpler and more flexible to operate. Scrap steel and 'sponge iron' are fed into the furnace. The liquid metal, at about 1600 degrees Celsius, is poured into a water-cooled copper mould from which the solid bar or strip is pulled continuously, a technique known as 'continuous casting'.

'Sponge iron' is used when insufficient scrap is available. It is made by removing the oxygen from iron ore pellets at 900 degrees Celsius in a stream of suitable gas, usually a hydrogen-carbon monoxide mixture. The pellets remain solid as they are converted into spongy chunks of iron ready to be melted in the steel furnace. As the gas can be made from coal or natural gas, the process is very suitable for developing countries lacking both scrap steel and the kind of coking coal needed for a conventional blast furnace.

But Nucor's success is not simply the result of getting in at the right time with modern technology. The whole ethos of the firm is novel. The production workers, all non-union, are paid below the union rates, but they can earn bonuses which often exceed their basic wage. It is a clean, tough game: excuses such as sickness or equipment failure do not count. Managers eat in the cafeteria, travel in the city by public transport, and take their chance with the rest on getting a place in the communal carpark. Workers are encouraged to keep their eyes open for any improvements which could increase production and, automatically, their bonus. They share in the prosperity of their firm though they don't share in the management decisions.

The result is that each Nucor worker takes on average about three hours to make a tonne of steel, as good as in a similar Japanese mill, and comparing with well over six in a normal American plant. In South Carolina the average Nucor worker was pulling in $30 000 a year when the United Steel Workers' average was $24 000 and the average hourly paid worker was getting less than $12 000. The stock market has recognized their success by pushing the share price up from $8 to $80 – the sort of treatment usually reserved for bioengineering, or those electronics, computing or aerospace firms with lucrative military contracts.

For in the 1980s the arms race, the prime invention of Alfred

Krupp, was entering its fastest and cruellest stage. With the US and the USSR well in the lead, France was running a poor third, while West Germany was overtaking the United Kingdom. Still more depressing, however, was the appearance of Third World countries as serious competitors: Argentina, Brazil, Israel, India, South Africa and Taiwan were making and selling arms to even poorer countries, although they all had agonizing human problems – food, housing, or employment – which were crying out for constructive action and not for the production of weapons.

In the developed countries of both East and West, public concern with the arms race was taking the form of big demonstrations against nuclear weapons. But to stop the race means overcoming an almost insuperable obstacle: the loss of jobs.

At present the workers and managers in the arms industries don't often look beyond the simple equation: arms manufacture equals jobs. In *The Arms Bazaar*, Anthony Sampson gives the response of Gerry Whipple, Californian regional director of the United Auto Workers, to his question about the B1 bomber. 'It's the best deterrent we have,' said the union leader.

It provides a very necessary job programme and it stimulates the aerospace industry. California has been built on food, defence and oil: you can't expect us to convert into industries for garbage disposal or cheap houses ... workers can't have pride in making low-cost housing, when the low-income families just use them for putting garbage in the hall. The people making the B1 bomber think they're working for the good of the community, and people have pride in it. This used to be the aerospace capital of the world, and now I reckon there's as much as 50 per cent unemployment ... As for exporting arms, if we didn't do it, someone else would: and without arms those countries would be totally defenceless.

Bernard Shaw's Andrew Undershaft could hardly have said it more clearly. Nonetheless, these sincere views will have to change if world peace is ever to be attained. Countering them is not difficult: during the debate on the B1 bomber, for example, a Chase Econometrics study was produced, showing that if the money spent on the B1 had been used instead for a tax cut it would have yielded 30 000 more jobs; or if spent on a housing programme, 70 000 more. The harder thing is to change the underlying attitudes.

Fortunately, the conversion in attitude doesn't have to wait for a light to shine on the armament workers, as it did for St Paul on the road to Damascus. The changes are already starting. In 1983 an aero-space conference, held by the International Metalworkers Fed-eration, declared that military production no longer means jobs: its president, William Winpisinger, also president of the US Asso-ciation of Machinists and Aerospace Workers, called for arms reduc-tions by all countries. 'All workers in the industrialized world,' he said, 'must collectively insist that their governments and employers plan for socially useful peaceful production alongside military production.'

A step in this direction came from a group of workers in the British company, Lucas Aerospace. They had been doing such things as designing components for military aircraft destined for the inter-national arms market. The ultimate futility of their work had given them a sense of frustration and, by a series of chance events, they became aware not only of what technology could do for the needs of humanity but also of how far short it was falling.

In their locality old people were actually dying in their homes through lack of a decent heating system; children with spinal disease were constricted in their movements to an excruciating degree; others were dying for want of a kidney machine.

So these Lucas workers evolved a plan which took advantage of their skills and the sophisticated facilities of Lucas to make a series of socially useful products: a heat pump to provide cheap domestic heating; a 'Hobcart' that spina bifida children could use to get around instead of just crawling on the floor; a microprocessed kidney machine that would be portable, and thus preserve the mobility and dignity of the patient; safety features for trains and cars; and similar products designed for people as well as for profit.

Not only were the products designed *for* people: they were designed *by* people, sophisticated engineers who found a high degree of fulfilment in their novel tasks. Mike Parry Evans said it was one of the most enriching experiences of his life when he took the Hobcart down and saw the expression on the face of a child with spina bifida. For the first time in his career he actually saw the person who was going to use the product he had designed. A pity that Gerry Whipple, of the United Auto Workers, wasn't there with him.

The economics of the plan were sound, perhaps even too logical and smacking of commonsense for the economic backwoodsmen running British industry in the twentieth century. Instead of sacking a worker making a kidney machine and paying out £40 a week for

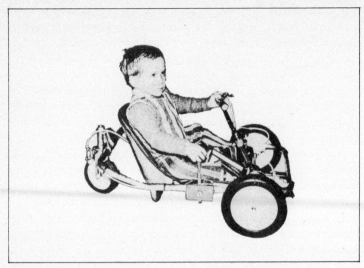

The 'Hobcart'. Lucas Aerospace workers' model of a mobile car
for crippled children, one of their 'socially useful products'

the dole, plus £30 for the administration of that dole, why not pay
the £70 to keep on making kidney machines and thereby saving
people's lives? The right of an individual to satisfying and meaning-
ful work was not necessarily an extravagance that the nation could
not afford.

The social and political implications brought opposition from
government, company and even from some unions: when an order
for 2000 Hobcarts arrived from the Spina Bifida Association of
Australia, the company refused to manufacture them, saying that
they were incompatible with its product range. In 1976 Lucas
declared that the employees' interests would best be served by
accepting its existing product policy: high-technology military
aerospace equipment. Two years later it announced 2000 re-
dundancies.

The resistance of management to giving away any of its power is
neither surprising nor new. It is the recognizable descendant of
Alfred Krupp's policy of dismissing any worker showing social
democratic tendencies. It is a struggle about democracy. As Bertrand
Russell said sixty years ago, 'There can be no real freedom or
democracy until the people who do the work in a business also

control its management.' The struggle may be expected to continue for at least another sixty years: deep-seated attitudes take a long time to turn round. But the Lucas workers have made a powerful demonstration, and similar schemes are being explored, for example, in the different contexts of Vickers and Rolls-Royce. Their ideas will continue to spread until not only the Krupps and the Carnegies, but also the descendants of the Lovedales, Schillers and Taines, the foundry-workers and cooks, the secretaries and scientists, all get a say in what their lives are actually achieving.

Meanwhile, away from the hurly-burly of social and political strife, scientists have been unravelling more of the mysteries of iron and blood. The deeper they go, the harder the search becomes, but successes are still being achieved. The advances in understanding the physical nature of iron are fascinating: they have brought us new materials which may add to the well-being of society, although with nothing like the revolutionary impact made by the discoveries of a Bessemer. But the advances in that subtle area of interaction between blood and iron can transform people's lives and sometimes make the difference between life and death.

One intriguing innovation is a method of making a metal into a glass. Metals are usually crystalline, and the finer the size of the crystal grains, the higher is the strength. Glass has no crystalline structure at all: nor has a liquid. So by cooling molten iron extremely rapidly – within a few thousandths of a second – the crystals don't have time to form, and it solidifies into a homogeneous, glass-like metal three or four times stronger than the best steel alloys. Even more striking and important is its resistance to corrosion – up to a hundred times better than stainless steel. The new material, first sold commercially under the name of 'Metglas', has many possible applications, although none of them constitutes a technological revolution. The day of dramatic changes from a single physical discovery may be over.

Affluent people are in little need of new physical powers, whether faster cars, quieter aeroplanes, brighter lighting or stereoscopic television; the poor are suffering for the lack of even the most meagre facilities of physical science and technology. Matters are very different in the life sciences. The great scourges of the human race – arthritis or cancer, for instance – are not respecters of persons: they cripple and kill rich and poor alike. One could imagine that the powers of science are being largely directed towards such matters, and also, to some extent, towards improving existing physical materials and processes, and lastly to some means of defence. One would be wrong.

In the United Kingdom, for instance, the 1982 science research budget of the Ministry of Defence stood at three *billion* dollars, more than three times as much as the research councils spent on medicine, agriculture, environment, engineering, computing, physics, astronomy and every other form of basic science in Britain put together. That is why four out of every ten scientists in Britain are working on military-related projects.

It does not immediately follow that the scientists are therefore responsible for the arms race. They have merely gone where the money is and where the jobs are. Certainly when they get there they seem to enjoy meeting the challenges of performance that military science demands, more rigorous and 'lateral' than in many civilian laboratories. But when you realize that most of these military scientists are men, you may wonder how far the *machismo* of guns, jet fighters, submarines and missiles is playing a part. Until the fourteenth century, the word *weapon* was synonymous with penis. 'While thou art young and thy weapon keen, wreak thee with wiving,' wrote Langlands in *Piers Plowman*.

Six centuries and innumerable wars later, W. H. Auden thought it beyond a joke: 'Today our phallic toys have become too dangerous to be tolerated. I see little hope for a peaceful world until men are excluded from the realm of foreign policy altogether, and all decisions concerning international relations are reserved for women . . .'

Despite the handicap of being a poor relation, medical research has been throwing some startling new light on the subtle relations between blood and iron. It is 300 years since it was discovered that iron was present in blood. Anaemic young women were treated by the remedy of Dr Sydenham, physician in Cromwell's army. Half a gram of iron filings, steeped in cold Rhine wine, to be taken daily: 'To the worn out or languid blood it gives a spur or filip whereby the animal spirits which before lay sunken and prostrate under their own weight are raised and excited. The pulse gains strength, the face (no longer pale and deathlike) a fresh ruddy colour.'

Though iron in some form remained the accepted 'tonic' to counter anaemia and weakness, recent research has cast doubts on the wisdom of such treatment. Iron is essential to the well-being of germs as well as of humans, and to counter anaemia unthinkingly with iron may turn a mild infection into a raging disease.

In that scourge of humanity, rheumatoid arthritis, iron is directly involved. As the inflammation and the pain develop, so the iron builds up in the membranes around a joint and in the fluid that lubricates it. It is not yet clear which is cause and which effect. Free iron is toxic to living cells and could be responsible for the destruction of cartilage and bone cells that can progress until the sufferer is crippled and deformed.

Under normal, healthy conditions, free iron would be snapped up and bound to a storage protein called *ferritin* to prevent it from causing any trouble. But each molecule of ferritin can only bind a maximum of 4500 atoms of iron, and well before it is saturated the toxicity of the iron starts to show through. A heavily iron-coated ferritin molecule thus becomes a source of damage. In health it acts as a storehouse of iron, located in liver or spleen, as part of the well-balanced iron cycle of our bodies. Our iron has to be balanced, and its absorption carefully controlled, because we have no mechanism for excreting it.

There is yet another source of damage once things start going wrong in this way. The most obvious role of iron in the blood is that of the oxygen carrier in the red cells. There is, however, a more subtle role in which the iron rides on a protein attached to one of the much rarer white cells, the *lymphocytes*. Although they are outnumbered a thousand-fold by the red cells, we still have about 2000 billion lymphocytes in our bodies, and the production factories in the marrow of our bones are replacing them at about one million a second. They are the most sophisticated of the three types of white cell responsible for immunity to specific diseases such as smallpox or diphtheria. Somehow – perhaps because of the freeloading iron atoms on their surface – they also pile up in the joints of a victim of arthritis and add to the inflammatory damage.

In this complex area, the scales are just beginning to fall from the scientists' eyes. A picture seems to be appearing of a superbly evolved metal-protein control system using three types of white blood cell and three different iron-binding proteins. This is the defence system which fights off invading armies of bacteria: when it goes wrong, however, it may produce havoc in the form of rheumatoid arthritis or of cancers such as Hodgkin's disease and leukemia.

We seem to have reached a cliff-hanger in the story of blood and iron. When will the next episode appear? Scientific progress is not directly proportional to the money spent on it, but a greater investment in the role of iron in blood would be reasonable. In the US alone, for instance, there are something like two million people disabled by rheumatoid arthritis. That is a vast amount of human suffering: it is also, though of less importance, a considerable economic loss to the community. A crude calculation shows that the economic 'return' from the expenditure on arthritis research could be about the same as the return from the exports of armaments, \$20 billion. But the amount spent on arthritis is dwarfed a thousand-fold by the \$200 billion spent on arms. As a purely economic proposition, the armaments industry offers only 0.1 per cent of the potential of medical science.

Unless you can believe that the 'security' purchased for the extra \$180 billion is really necessary, the gap between the figures is remarkable. It is still easier to get money for the spilling of blood than for the saving of it. But there is hope for the future in those figures, which reflect the enormous productivity of a modern industrial society. If only 1 per cent of the US arms bill were to be converted, it could increase the effort on arthritis ten-fold.

That is probably more than the system would need or, indeed, could handle. There would be plenty over for conversion to a society that prefers to use its iron for bridges rather than tanks, a step forward from the Hittites who first dug it out of the ground and who could think of little better to do with it than to threaten their neighbours.

Letter from Brazil

Hotel Carioca,
Rio de Janeiro,
14 June 2002

Dear Professor Lovedale (!),

Sorry about the formality – I've just heard of your appointment as Professor of Steel Science, and I couldn't wait to see it written down! Derek spotted the news item while he was looking through *Nature* in the Institute library before we left São Paulo yesterday, and he made a rather cruel joke. 'I suppose it'll be in the Department of History,' he said. Just like a cocky plastics man! But the Materials conference showed him that steel's not dead yet – if he was listening, that is.

I did wish that you'd been there, though. It really was fantastic – quite different from any meeting I've ever been to. Emilio Funes came for the opening and made a great speech about science serving the people! He certainly has a way with him, and you begin to see why they call him the Christ from the Andes. He's even persuaded the IMF that with the mass support he's got he can cure Brazil's inflation and unemployment, and they're going to make low-interest loans on *his* terms instead of theirs.

He brought a number of people with him from his ruling party, the *Partido dos Trabalhadores*, as far as I can sort it out a Christian-socialist mixture of the peasants' and the Catholic workers' parties. And they actually joined in the following sessions! They kept bringing the discussion back to how the research could help the ordinary people of Brazil. Most of these arguments went on in sections like rubber and plastics, or in odd groups like the one on 'the use of cane waste in housing materials', but they also got into the section on metals. It was quite funny to see the serious scientists from the United German Republic having to explain how their phase diagrams would help the steelworkers in the Volta Redonda!

Must dash now. We're off to the Folk Museum this afternoon and our friends from the Institute are taking us to a cabaret tonight overlooking the bay. Old Arndt von Bohlen sometimes dines there – he's quite a character on the local scene, apparently, and tells amazing stories of the old days in Germany, though he hasn't got any connection nowadays with the Krupp-Thyssen business.

Congratulations again, and best wishes

Han Fei Ma

Author's Note

The mixture of fact and fiction in this book owes much to a wide range of literature as well as to stimulating inputs from many people. Of the books that I have found most valuable, William Manchester's *The Arms of Krupp* is outstanding; in *The Arms Bazaar*, Anthony Sampson provides a sobering insight into the current state of the arms race, while, on the cheerful side, June Goodfield's *An Imagined World* shows what women can do in the more benevolent field of medical research.

My individual debts extend first to Jane Arms and Jackie Yowell, of Penguin Books. Dr Bill Beech introduced me to the splendid social museum of the city of Sheffield. For contributions of various but invaluable kinds I am grateful to Kenneth Barraclough, Maurice Bazin, Maurice Clegg, Edith Cloutman, Mike Cooley, Steve Cooper, Coralie Creevey, Earl Hackett, Jack Legge, Ali Lyssa, Deirdre Mason, Paul Mason, Michael Moore, Marlene Norst, Hugh Philp, Chloë Refshauge, Anita Rimel, Mort Shearer, Dan Weaver and Chris Wilder.

I have made use of a number of imaginary characters, in particular the Lovedales, the Schillers, and the Taines; others, such as Adolf Hitler or the various Krupps, were well beyond my imagining, though without them it would have been a very different story.

Peter Mason
Sydney, 1984

Acknowledgements

The author and publisher wish to thank the following copyright holders for permission to reproduce their material: Aerospatiale, 171; Bibliothèque Nationale, Paris, 51; Bismarck Museum, Hamburg, 62; Chatto & Windus, and the estate of Harold Owen, 103; Mike Cooley, 178; Firth, Brown, Ltd, Sheffield, 18; Gilbert Frankau, 'The Voice of the Guns', from *The City of Fear*, 1917, 104; The Library of Congress, 25; Her Majesty's Stationery Office, London, 151; Imperial War Museum, London, title page, 87, 102, 135, 145; MARS, 49; Deirdre Mason, 54; Sheffield City Council, 16, 35; Sheffield Forgemasters Ltd, archive photographs, 16, 18; Yevgeny Yevtushenko and William Collins, London, 153.

Index